Edexcel

GCSE MODULAR MATHEMATICS
Examples and Practice

HIGHER

Stage 1

Heinemann

Edexcel
Success through qualifications

About this book

This *Examples and Practice* book is designed to help you get the best possible grade in your Edexcel GCSE maths examination. The authors are senior examiners and coursework moderators and have a good understanding of Edexcel's requirements.

Higher Stage 1 Examples and Practice covers all the topics that will be tested in your Higher Stage 1 examination. You can use this book to revise in the run up to your exam, or you can use it throughout the course, alongside the *Edexcel GCSE Maths* Higher core textbook.

References in the contents list for each section of the book tell you where to find the most relevant paragraph of the specification. For example, NA2a refers to Number and Algebra, paragraph 2, section a.

Helping you prepare for your exam

To help you prepare, each topic offers:
- **Key points** to reinforce the key teaching concepts
- **Teaching references** showing you where the relevant material is covered in both the old and new editions of the *Edexcel GCSE Maths* Higher core textbook. These references show you where to find full explanations of concepts, and additional worked examples e.g.

> Teaching reference:
> (*pp 47–49, section 3.1, 3.2*) — The first reference is to the old edition
> pp 53–56, section 3.2, 3.3 — The second reference is to the new edition

Which edition am I using?

The new editions of the *Edexcel GCSE Maths* core textbooks have yellow cover flashes saying "ideal for the 2001 specification". You can also use the old edition (no yellow cover flash) to help you prepare for your Stage 1 exam.

Where material is new to the new specification there is no reference to the old edition textbooks.
- **Worked examples** showing you how to tackle a problem and lay out your answer
- **Exercises** with references showing you which exercises in the *Edexcel GCSE Maths* Higher core textbook contain similar questions. The first reference, in brackets and italic, is to the old edition. The second reference is to the new edition
- **A summary of key points** so you can check that you have covered all the key concepts

Exam practice and using the answers

An exam style practice paper at the back of the book will help you make sure that you are totally exam-ready. This paper is exactly the same length and standard as your actual Stage 1 exam.

Answers to all the questions are provided at the back of the book. Once you have completed an exercise you can use the answers to check whether you have made any mistakes. You need to show full working in your exam – it isn't enough to write down the answer.

Contents

Heinemann Educational Publishers
Halley Court, Jordan Hill, Oxford OX2 8EJ
Part of Harcourt Education

Heinemann is the registered trademark of Harcourt Education Limited

First Published 2001

ISBN 0 435 53539 0

05 04 03
10 9 8 7 6 5 4

Designed and typeset by Tech-Set Ltd, Gateshead, Tyne and Wear
Cover design by Miller, Craig and Cocking
Cover photo: Photodisc
Printed in the United Kingdom by Scotprint

Acknowledgements
The publishers and authors would like to thank Jean Linsky for her contribution and assistance with the manuscript.

The answers are not the responsibility of Edexcel.

Publishing team	Design	Production	Author team
Editorial	Phil Richards	David Lawrence	Karen Hughes
Sue Bennett	Colette Jacquelin	Jason Wyatt	Trevor Johnson
Lauren Bourque			Peter Jolly
Des Brady			David Kent
Nicholas Georgiou			Keith Pledger
Maggie Rumble			
Nick Sample			
Harry Smith			
Isabel Thomas			

Tel: 01865 888058 www.heinemann.co.uk

1 Standard form, powers, fractions and decimals

1.1 Prime factor decomposition, HCF and LCM

Example 1

Express 1008 as the product of its prime factors.

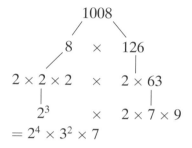

$$= 2^4 \times 3^2 \times 7$$

> The number is even so 2 is a factor:
> $$1008 = 2 \times 504$$
> If you spot a larger factor then use it to speed up the process.

Prime factor decomposition is a good way of finding the HCF (highest common factor) and LCM (lowest common multiple).

Example 2

Find the HCF and LCM for 24, 78 and 182.
First factorize:

$$24 = 2 \times 2 \times 2 \times 3$$
$$78 = 2 \times 3 \times 13$$
$$282 = 2 \times 3 \times 47$$

HCF = 6 (the common factors are 2 and 3)

The LCM requires *all* of the factors for each number *but* does not need to repeat them if they are already included from one of the other numbers, i.e. only three of the 2s are needed.

$$\text{LCM} = 2 \times 2 \times 2 \times 3 \times 13 \times 47 = 14\,664$$

Exercise 1A   Links (*1B, 1C, 1D*) 1B, 1C, 1D

1 Write the following numbers in prime factor form:
   (a) 36   **(b)** 200   **(c)** 75   **(d)** 675   **(e)** 196
   (f) 108   **(g)** 572   **(h)** 784   **(i)** 968   **(j)** 2016
   (k) 5929   **(l)** 2156   **(m)** 288   **(n)** 8000   **(o)** 7600

2 Find the HCF and LCM of the following sets of numbers:

  (a) 24, 36

  (b) 15, 75

  (c) 20, 45

  (d) 27, 90

  (e) 140, 210

  (f) 42, 35

  (g) 15, 35, 60

  (h) 28, 70, 98

  (i) 42, 63, 105

  (j) 16, 32, 48

1.2 Index laws with positive integer powers

■ $a^x \times a^y = a^{x+y}$

■ $a^x \div a^y = a^{x-y}$

Example 3

Simplify

(a) $a^7 \times a^4$

(b) $a^6 \div a^4$

(a) $a^7 \times a^4 = a^{7+4} = a^{11}$

(b) $a^6 \div a^4 = a^{6-4} = a^2$

Exercise 1B   **Links (*1G, 20A, 20B*) 1F, 1G**

1 Simplify, then use your calculator to evaluate

  (a) $2^7 \times 2^3$

  (b) $3^8 \times 3^4$

  (c) $5^2 \times 5^6$

  (d) $4^3 \times 4^2 \times 4^2$

  (e) $2^3 \times 2^4 \times 2^5$

  (f) $3^8 \div 3^2$

  (g) $7^9 \div 7^6$

  (h) $6^4 \div 6^3$

  (i) $11^{16} \div 11^{12}$

  (j) $4^5 \div 4^5$

2 Simplify these algebraic expressions:

  (a) $x^2 \times x^3$

  (b) $x^4 \times x^5$

  (c) $y^7 \div y^2$

  (d) $y^9 \div y^3$

  (e) $2x^3 \times 3x^4$

  (f) $3y^2 \times 4y^5$

  (g) $6y^8 \div 3y^6$

  (h) $12k^4 \div 3k^3$

  (i) $xy^2 \times x^2y^3$

  (j) $a^3b^2 \times ab$

  (k) $p^4q^3 \times p^2q$

  (l) $\dfrac{x^2y^5}{xy^2}$

  (m) $\dfrac{p^4q^3}{p^2q^3}$

  (n) $\dfrac{6a^5b^3}{3ab}$

  (o) $\dfrac{2a^4b \times 3ab^5}{6a^2b^2}$

  (p) $\dfrac{4a^3b^2 \times 3a^2b^3}{6a^4b^4}$

  (q) $(x+y)^3 \times (x+y)^2$

  (r) $\dfrac{(2x+y)^5}{(2x+y)^3}$

1.3 Standard form

■ A number in standard form is $A \times 10^n$ where $0 < A < 10$ and n is an integer.

Example 4

Write in standard form
(a) 236 000 and (b) 0.010 63.
Write as a decimal number
(c) 2.01×10^7 and (d) 5.7×10^{-3}.

(a) $236\,000 = 2\,\overrightarrow{36000} = 2.36 \times 10^5$
$\underbrace{}_{5}$

(b) $0.010\,63 = 0.\overleftarrow{01}\,063 = 1.063 \times 10^{-2}$
$\underbrace{}_{-2}$

(c) 2.01×10^7

Build on 7 decimal places from the decimal point:
$2\,\underline{0100000} = 20\,100\,000$
$\quad\ _{7}$

(d) 5.7×10^{-3}

Work back 3 decimal places from the decimal point:
$\underline{005}\,7 = 0.0057$
$_{-3}$

Exercise 1C   Links (5N, 5O, 5P) 5O, 5P

1 Write the following numbers in standard form:
(a) 30 000, 400, 0.006, 0.000 08.
(b) 2170, 63, 71 000, 0.761.
(c) 203, 50 030, 0.009 01, 0.0101.

2 Write the following numbers as decimal numbers:
(a) 3.1×10^2 (b) 2.6×10^4
(c) 8.9×10^1 (d) 6.7×10^{-1}
(e) 1.57×10^{-3} (f) 2.04×10^{-4}
(g) 1.003×10^2 (h) 3.060×10^1
(i) 7.0103×10^{-3} (j) 4.079×10^{-2}

3 Write your answers to question 2 to 1 significant figure.

1.4 Multiply and divide fractions

Example 5

Work out $1\frac{7}{9} \times 3\frac{3}{8}$.

$\dfrac{\overset{2}{\cancel{16}}}{\underset{1}{\cancel{9}}} \times \dfrac{\overset{3}{\cancel{27}}}{\underset{1}{\cancel{8}}} = 6$ Step 1: change to improper fractions.
Step 2: cancel where possible.

Example 6

Work out $3\frac{5}{7} \div 5\frac{5}{21}$.

$$\frac{26}{7} \div \frac{110}{21}$$

$$\frac{\overset{13}{\cancel{26}}}{\underset{1}{\cancel{7}}} \times \frac{\overset{3}{\cancel{21}}}{\underset{55}{\cancel{110}}} = \frac{39}{55}$$

Step 1: change to improper fractions.
Step 2: inverse of $\div$ is $\times$.
  inverse of $\frac{110}{21}$ is $\frac{21}{110}$.
Step 3: cancel where possible.

Exercise 1D

In the following questions, simplify as fully as possible:

1   $3\frac{3}{4} \times 2\frac{1}{5}$

2   $8\frac{1}{3} \times 4\frac{1}{5}$

3   $5\frac{3}{5} \times 1\frac{3}{7}$

4   $3\frac{1}{5} \times 1\frac{1}{8}$

5   $1\frac{2}{7} \times 2\frac{2}{3}$

6   $2\frac{5}{18} \times 4\frac{1}{2}$

7   $4\frac{11}{16} \times 5\frac{3}{25}$

8   $1\frac{1}{2} \times 1\frac{1}{4} \times 1\frac{3}{5}$

9   $2\frac{2}{3} \times 1\frac{11}{16} \times 1\frac{5}{9}$

10   $2\frac{2}{3}(3\frac{5}{8} - 2\frac{1}{5})$

11   $1\frac{3}{5} \div \frac{4}{5}$

12   $3\frac{6}{7} \div 2\frac{4}{7}$

13   $4\frac{4}{5} \div 2\frac{2}{15}$

14   $1\frac{9}{16} \div 2\frac{1}{2}$

15   $9\frac{4}{5} \div \frac{7}{20}$

16   $1\frac{6}{7} \div 4\frac{16}{35}$

17   $4\frac{5}{7} \div 2\frac{1}{5}$

18   $7\frac{1}{4} \div 8\frac{2}{7}$

1.5 Fractions and decimals

Fractions can be changed to decimals by doing the division.
If the denominator only has 2s and 5s when in prime factor form
the decimal terminates. Otherwise the decimal is recurring.

Example 7

Turn these fractions into decimals:

(a) $\frac{7}{160}$ (b) $\frac{5}{13}$

(a) $7 \div 160$
  $= 0.043\,75$

(b) $5 \div 13$
  $= 0.\overset{.}{3}846\overset{.}{1}5\ldots$

> $160 = 2^5 \times 5$
> The decimal terminates.

> The decimal recurs.

Recurring decimals can be converted to fractions.

Example 8

Turn $0.\overset{.}{3}6\overset{.}{1}\ldots$ into a fraction.

$$s = 0.361\,361\,\overset{.}{3}6\overset{.}{1}\ldots$$
$$1000s = 361.361\,361\ldots$$
Subtract s: $999s = 361$
$$s = \frac{361}{999}$$

> $\times 1000$ because the decimal
> has 3 recurring digits.

Exercise 1E   Links *(23A, 23B)* 23A, 23B

1 Use a calculator to convert each of the following fractions to a decimal:

(a) $\frac{3}{8}$ (b) $\frac{7}{64}$ (c) $\frac{17}{25}$ (d) $\frac{97}{125}$

(e) $\frac{217}{625}$ (f) $\frac{7}{24}$ (g) $\frac{8}{33}$ (h) $\frac{7}{13}$

(i) $\frac{3}{22}$ (j) $\frac{77}{121}$ (k) $\frac{271}{999}$ (l) $\frac{14}{39}$

2 Find the fraction which is equal to the recurring decimals. Simplify as fully as possible.

(a) $0.1\dot{1}\ldots$ (b) $0.6\dot{3}\dot{6}\ldots$

(c) $0.3\dot{1}\ldots$ (d) $0.216\,\dot{2}1\dot{6}\ldots$

(e) $0.45\dot{4}\dot{5}\ldots$ (f) $0.1\dot{3}1\dot{4}\ldots$

(g) $0.147\,\dot{1}4\dot{7}\ldots$ (h) $0.\dot{7}40\,7\dot{4}\ldots$

(i) $0.642\,3\dot{2}\dot{3}\ldots$ (j) $0.561\dot{1}\ldots$

1.6 Estimating and checking

It is always useful to have a rough idea of the answer to a calculation. Sometimes you do not need to know the exact answer. Other times you may want to check whether the exact answer given is actually likely to be correct. An estimate does that for you.

Example 9

A tin of emulsion paint says that it covers $19.6\,\text{m}^2$. The room to be done has a perimeter of 13.2 m and a height of 2.8 m. Is one tin of paint enough? If not, how many will be needed?

$$\text{Number of tins required} = \frac{\text{Area}}{19.6} = \frac{13.2 \times 2.8}{19.6}$$

$$\simeq \frac{13 \times 3}{20} = \frac{39}{20} \simeq 2$$

As you do not paint the door or windows 2 tins should be enough.

Example 10

You are on the phone to your stockbroker to sell 623 shares. He says they sell at £7.92 per share.

The income will be $623 \times £7.92$.

This is roughly $600 \times 8 = £4800$

• 1 significant figure is accurate enough for most estimating.

However, if the question were 'Will this raise £5000?' you could do $625 \times 8 = £5000$ in your head as a better estimate.

You have increased the number of shares and the price. The answer to the question is 'No'.

Two useful facts when estimating

- When multiplying by a positive number less than 1 the answer will be smaller.
- When dividing by a positive number less than one the answer will be bigger.

Example 11

$$729 \times 0.93 = 736.56 \quad \text{Is this correct?}$$

Answer: It must be wrong:
$$729 \times 0.93 < 729$$

Actually the number 792 was keyed into the calculator by mistake. This type of error is quite common.

Example 12

Estimate $637 \div 0.87$.

Firstly, you know the answer must be greater than 637.

For your estimate you can use $630 \div 0.9$ (choosing numbers you can do in your head)

$$\simeq 700$$

(You can also deduce that the exact answer is more than 700 because using 630 instead of 637 makes a smaller answer, and using 0.9 instead of 0.87 also makes a smaller answer.)

Exercise 1F   **Links (*12D*) 12D**

1   Use 1 s.f. approximations to estimate
   (a) 37.62×0.315 **(b)** 0.761×827
   (c) 911.7×0.026 **(d)** 5.309×0.689
   (e) $15.72 \div 0.513$ **(f)** $8.37 \div 0.387$
   (g) $1.209 \div 0.097$ **(h)** $721 \div 0.068$

2   Without a calculator, work out:
   (a) $\dfrac{15 \times 4}{0.2}$ **(b)** $\dfrac{270}{0.03}$ **(c)** $\dfrac{29.1 + 6.9}{0.6}$

   (d) 0.2×60 **(e)** 0.3×0.6 **(f)** 25×0.6

3   Use suitable approximations to estimate the value of the following:
   (a) $\dfrac{28.32 \times 71.9}{5.603}$ **(b)** $\dfrac{\sqrt{17.3} \times 34.1}{8.26}$

   (c) $(3.19)^2 \times \sqrt{27.9}$ **(d)** $\dfrac{72.3 + 29.08}{51.2 - 49.3}$

   (e) $\dfrac{18.2}{0.35}$ **(f)** $\dfrac{58.2}{0.8}$

4 Estimate the value of the following. Say whether your estimate is bigger or smaller than the exact answer.

(a) $\dfrac{17.6 \times \sqrt{19.32} - 2.19}{0.19}$

(b) $\dfrac{(2.37 - 0.52)^3}{\sqrt{8.231}}$

(c) $\sqrt{15.3} - (2.1 \times 0.49)$

(d) $\dfrac{(7.836)^2 - (2.092)^2}{\sqrt{7.63 + 18.19}}$

5 Estimate how long it takes to travel 423 km at 0.72 km/min.

6 Estimate the value of 217 shares at 43p each.

7 Estimate the cost of 2327 units of electricity at 7.19p per unit.

8 Estimate how long it takes to fill a 100 litre tank at 0.62 litres per second.

9 Estimate how many seconds there are in a week.

10 A plant grows, on average, 0.013 mm/minute.
Estimate **(i)** how much it grows in an hour,
(ii) how much it grows in a day (24 hours).

Summary of key points

- $a^x \times a^y = a^{x+y}$
- $a^x \div a^y = a^{x-y}$
- A number in standard form is $A \times 10^n$ where $0 < A < 10$ and n is an integer.
- 1 significant figure is accurate enough for most estimating
- When multiplying by a positive number less than 1 the answer will be smaller.
- When dividing by a positive number less than 1 the answer will be bigger.

2 Percentage, ratio and proportion

2.1 Increasing and decreasing quantities by a percentage

■ To find a percentage of a quantity change the percentage into a decimal and multiply it by the quantity.

■ If an amount is increased by $x\%$ the new amount is $(100 + x)\%$ of the original amount.

■ If an amount is decreased by $x\%$ the new amount is $(100 - x)\%$ of the original amount.

Example 1

Calculate
(a) 30% of 90
(b) $17\frac{1}{2}\%$ of £50.

(a) Change 30% to a decimal and multiply:
$$30\% \text{ of } 90 = 0.3 \times 90$$
$$= 27$$
(b) $17\frac{1}{2}\%$ of £50 $= 0.175 \times 50$
$$= £8.75$$

Example 2

Lucy earns £11 000 per year.
She has to pay 22% income tax.
Calculate her earnings after tax.

As a percentage of original earnings her earnings after tax are
$(100 - 22)\% = 78\%$
78 as a decimal is 0.78
Her earnings after tax will be $0.78 \times £11\,000$
$$= £8580$$

Example 3

Lucy gets a 10% pay rise.
Before the rise she was earning £11 000. What is her new salary?

As a percentage of her old salary her new salary is $(100 + 10)\%$.
110% as a decimal $= 1.1$.
So her new salary will be $1.1 \times £11\,000$
$$= £12\,100$$

| **Exercise 2A** | **Links (5A, 5B, 5C) 5A, 5B, 5C** |

1 Calculate
   (a) 40% of 70   (b) 35% of 30   (c) $17\frac{1}{2}$% of £30
   (d) $33\frac{1}{2}$% of £81   (e) $12\frac{1}{2}$% of £4.80.

2 Write the new value as a percentage of the old value if
   (a) a car decreases in value by 18%
   (b) the cost of a coat increases by $12\frac{1}{2}$%
   (c) the cost of a holiday increases by 20%
   (d) the value of a computer decreases by $33\frac{1}{3}$%
   (e) a baby increases its weight by $17\frac{1}{2}$%.

3 In the first year of ownership a new car's value decreases by 12%. Calculate the value of a car after 1 year if it cost £7000 when new.

4 A sofa is sold at a discount of 30%. What is the price after discount if the original cost was £300?

5 Graham is given a $12\frac{1}{2}$% pay rise.
   Calculate his new salary if his original salary was £18 400.

6 Mr and Mrs Rodgers buy a house for £90 000. Calculate the selling price of the house if they sell it at a 23% profit.

7 Kate buys a house for £70 000. During the first year that she lives in the house its value increases by 7%. During the second year its value decreases by 4%. Calculate the value of the house at the end of the two years.

8 £400 is put in a savings account. During the first year 4% interest is added. During the second year 3% interest is added. How much is in the savings account at the end of the two years?

2.2 Percentage change

■ **When a quantity changes (increases or decreases) find the percentage change using**

$$\text{percentage change} = \frac{\text{actual change}}{\text{original quantity}} \times 100\%$$

Example 4

A car is bought for £4800 and sold for £3600.
Calculate the percentage loss on the car.

$$\text{Original price} = £4800$$
$$\text{Loss} = £4800 - £3600 = £1200$$

$$\text{percentage loss} = \frac{£1200}{£4800} \times 100\%$$
$$= 25\%$$

Exercise 2B	**Links (5D, 5E) 5D, 5E**

1 The weight of a packet of crisps is increased from 25 g to 30 g. Calculate the percentage increase in weight.

2 A marathon runner weighing 78 kg loses 3.5 kg due to fluid loss during a race. Calculate his percentage decrease in weight.

3 A computer is bought for £560. It is sold 3 years later for £364. Calculate the percentage loss.

4 A shopkeeper buys potatoes for 60p per kg. He sells them for 70p per kg. Calculate his percentage profit.

5 A dress that normally costs £45 is sold in a sale for £30. Calculate the percentage discount.

6 A car is bought for £8500 and sold for £6545 2 years later. Calculate the depreciation over the 2 years.

7 Jim bought 1000 shares at 22p per share. He sold all the shares for £200. Calculate his percentage loss to the nearest percent.

8 A ticket for a pop concert costs £25. The concert promoter makes £8 profit on each ticket sold. Calculate the promoter's percentage profit.

2.3 Reverse percentages

Teaching reference: (*p 97, section 5.5*) pp 100–101, section 5.5

Example 5

A restaurant bill includes a 10% service charge.
The bill is for £28.93.
Calculate the cost of the food before the service charge was added.

The bill is $(100 + 10)\% = 110\%$ of the cost of the food before the service charge
$$= 1.1 \text{ in decimal form}$$

so the bill is $1.1 \times$ cost of the food before service charge.

So $£28.93 = 1.1 \times$ cost of the food before service charge

$$\frac{£28.93}{1.1} = \text{cost of the food before service charge}$$

$$£26.30 = \text{cost of the food before service charge}$$

Exercise 2C	**Links (5F) 5F**

1 The price of a CD player is reduced by 15% in a sale. The sale price of the CD player is £102. Calculate the price of the CD player before the sale.

2   A house is sold for £138 000. The sellers make a 15% profit.
    How much did the house cost originally?

3   Peter pays 22% tax on his salary. After paying tax, Peter earns
    £16 280. Calculate Peter's original salary.

4   The weight of a beefburger decreases by 12% during cooking.
    The cooked weight of the beefburger is 230 g.
    What was the uncooked weight of the beefburger?

5   A book sells for £15. This includes a 20% profit for the publisher.
    How much does the book cost before the profit is added?

6   The total cost of a CD is £11.75 including VAT at $17\frac{1}{2}$%.
    Calculate the cost of the CD before VAT is added.

2.4 Repeated percentage change

■   **Compound interest is interest paid on an amount and on the
    interest on that amount.**

Example 6

Mary invests £300 in a savings account. The account pays 5%
interest per annum. She leaves her money in the account for
10 years.

(a) By what single number can £300 be multiplied by to find the
     amount of money in the savings account after 10 years?

(b) How much money is in Mary's account after 10 years?

(a) The account pays 5% per annum.
     The percentage increase after 1 year is $(100 + 5)$%.
     Written as a decimal this is 1.05.
     This percentage increase is applied again in the next year.
     So the total percentage increase after 2 years is
     1.05×1.05 or $(1.05)^2$.
     This will happen every year for 10 years. So after the 10 years
     the percentage increase will be $(1.05)^{10}$.

(b) Mary's savings at the end of 10 years will be
     $$£300 \times (1.05)^{10} = £488.67 \text{ to the nearest penny}$$

Exercise 2D   Links (5G) 5H

1   Jessica invests £500 in a building society account on the 1st of
    January. The building society pays interest on the account at
    the rate of 6.3% per annum.
    Calculate the amount of money in the account at the end of
    (a) 1 year
    (b) 3 years
    (c) 5 years.

2 Malcolm invests £1250 in a bank account for 5 years at a rate of interest of 7.5% per annum.
Calculate the amount of interest that will be earned over the 5 year period.

3 Julie earns a salary of £12 000. At the end of each year she is given a 4% pay rise.
Calculate Julie's salary after 5 years.

4 Karen invests £500 in a savings account at the rate of 8% per annum. How long will it take Karen's investment to reach £700?

5 Phil takes a 25 year fixed rate mortgage for £40 000. The mortgage rate is 3.5% per annum.
   (a) Write down the single number that £40 000 must be multiplied by to calculate the total amount repaid by Phil.
   (b) Write down the total amount repaid by Phil.

6 A population of rabbits increases by 10% every 2 weeks.
At the beginning of March the population is 16. Assuming no rabbit dies, how many rabbits will there be after 20 weeks?

7 Samina discovers that her grandfather invested £25 in a savings account at a rate of 8% per annum 50 years ago and forgot about it.
How much will be in the account 50 years after the initial investment?

2.5 Ratios

■ **You can use ratios to show how things are divided or shared.**

Example 7

Jill, Lesley and Marcia share £600 in the ratio of their ages.
Jill is 16, Lesley 18 and Marcia 26.

(a) In what ratio do they share the money?
(b) Calculate the amount of money each girl receives.

(a) They share the money in the ratio 16 : 18 : 26.
   In its simplest form this is 8 : 9 : 13.
(b) Sharing in the ratio 8 : 9 : 13 means the money is divided into 30 parts with Jill getting 8 parts, Lesley 9 parts and Marcia 13 parts.

$$\text{So Jill gets } \tfrac{8}{30} \times £600 = £160$$
$$\text{Lesley gets } \tfrac{9}{30} \times £600 = £180$$
$$\text{Marcia gets } \tfrac{13}{30} \times £600 = £260$$

1   The ratio of nuts and fruits to other ingredients in a packet of muesli is 2 : 3.
   (a) What fraction of the muesli is nuts and fruits?
   (b) Calculate the weight of nuts and fruits in a packet of muesli weighing 350 g.

2   George, Mark and John earn £60 for doing some gardening. They share the money in the ratio of the hours each boy spent working. George worked for 5 hours, Mark for 3 hours and John for 2 hours.
   Work out the amount of money each boy should receive.

3   A video shop has comedy, horror and action videos in the ratio 1 : 3 : 5. The shop has a total of 1800 videos.
   (a) What fraction of the videos are horror videos?
   (b) What fraction of the videos are comedy videos?
   (c) How many action videos does the shop have?

4   A box of 42 chocolates contains milk, plain and white chocolates in the ratio 3 : 2 : 1.
   (a) What fraction of the chocolates are plain?
   (b) How many milk chocolates are contained in the box?

5   It is written on a packet of sweet pea seeds that the ratio of pink, purple and white flowers is 5 : 4 : 2.
   (a) How many purple flowers would you expect from a packet of 110 seeds?
   (b) What fraction of the flowers would you expect to be white?

Example 8

Concrete is made from gravel, cement and sand in the ratio 3 : 2 : 1.
A mixture of concrete is made using 12 kg of cement.
Calculate the amounts of the other items required for the mixture.

Cement is $\frac{2}{6}$ of the total mixture.

   So $\frac{2}{6} = 12$ kg

   $\frac{1}{6} = 6$ kg

The mixture needs to have $\frac{3}{6}$ gravel and $\frac{1}{6}$ sand.

   So the amounts required are
      gravel 3×6 kg $= 18$ kg
      sand 1×6 kg $= 6$ kg

Exercise 2F   **Links** (*5M*) **5N**

1   A recipe for buns states that flour, fat and sugar should be
    used in the ratio 4 : 2 : 1.
    A cook uses 300 g of flour.
    How much of each of the other ingredients should she use?

2   Bridget, Keith and David share a cash prize in the ratio of
    2 : 5 : 6. David wins £60. Find
    (a) how much Bridget wins,
    (b) the total amount of the prize money.

3   A chemical compound is made from 3 elements A, B and C in
    the ratio 2 : 5 : 7.
    2.6 mg of element A is used. Find
    (a) how much of element C is required,
    (b) the total weight of the compound.

4   A box of sweets contains pink, blue and green sweets.
    $\frac{1}{4}$ of the sweets are pink, $\frac{3}{5}$ of the sweets are blue.
    (a) What fraction of the sweets are green?
    (b) In what ratio are the different coloured sweets contained
          in the box?
    (c) The box contains 15 pink sweets. How many of each of
          the other colours of sweet are in the box?

5   £600 is shared between Paul, Douglas and Gillian in the ratio
    2 : x : 4x. Paul receives £100.
    (a) Find the value of x.
    (b) Calculate how much Douglas and Gillian receive.

2.6 Direct and inverse proportion

■   **Two quantities are in direct proportion if their ratio stays the
    same as the quantities increase or decrease.**

■   **Two quantities are in inverse proportion when one increases
    at the same rate as the other decreases.**

Example 9

A car uses seven litres of petrol to travel 84 km. If the amount of
petrol used is in direct proportion to the distance travelled, how far
can the car travel on five litres?

    7l gives 84 km of travel

    So   1l gives $\dfrac{84 \text{ km}}{7} = 12 \text{ km}$

    and 5l gives 12 km × 5 = 60 km

Example 10

If three women take 15 days to build a house how long will it take five women?

3 women take 15 days

1 woman takes $15 \times 3 = 45$ days

5 women take $45 \div 5 = 9$ days

Exercise 2G

1 Six books cost £24. How much will
   (a) 1 book cost?
   (b) 8 books cost?

2 Verity is paid £56.80 for working eight hours. How much will Verity be paid for working 3 hours?

3 Twenty bales of hay will feed five horses for twenty days. How long will twenty bales of hay feed:
   (a) 1 horse?
   (b) 4 horses?

4 Three dressmakers can make six bridesmaid dresses in five days. How long will it take 5 dressmakers to make six bridesmaid dresses?

5 The recipe for 24 shortcake biscuits requires the following ingredients:
   8 oz flour, 4 oz butter, 2 oz sugar.
   What amount of each of the ingredients will be required to make 30 biscuits?

6 A student can write 400 words in 2 hours. How long will a 100 word essay take the student to write?

7 A bottle of shower gel lasts a family of four 9 days. How long will the same bottle of shower gel last a family of six?

8 A packet of hamster food lasts five hamsters fifteen days. How long will the same packet of food last eight hamsters to the nearest day?

9 Five packets of sweets cost £1.90. How much will eight packets of the same sweets cost?

10 Two workmen can complete a job in seven hours. How long will it take three workmen to complete the same job?

Exercise 2H   Mixed questions

1

> ## *SPECIAL OFFER*
> ### *Digital cameras only £435 + VAT*

If VAT is $17\frac{1}{2}\%$, calculate the total cost of the digital camera.

2 A photocopier produces a copy of an original sheet of paper that is reduced by 42%. If the area of the original sheet of paper is $600\,\text{cm}^2$ what is the area of the copy?

3 A shopkeeper buys a cooker for £180. He sells it for £207. Calculate his percentage profit.

4 Deepa bought a car for £8600. She sold the car for £6700 two years later. Calculate her percentage loss.

5 All items in a sale are reduced by 30%. Alex bought a coat in the sale for £135.
Work out the pre-sale price of the coat.

6 On the 1st of January Eryl invests £700 in a building society savings account. The account pays interest at the rate of 5.5% per annum.
Calculate the total amount of interest earned after 5 years.

7 The population of the world is growing at the rate of 1.5% per annum. What single number can be used to calculate the world population growth over 50 years?

8 Paula, Sasha and Luisa share £4500 in the ratio $2 : 5 : 8$.
(a) What fraction of the money does Sasha receive?
(b) How much money does Luisa receive?

9 Flour, butter and sugar are used in the ratio $5 : 4 : 2$ to make shortcake. Nicolette only has $200\,\text{g}$ of butter.
How much flour and sugar should she use?

10 A fizzy drink is made using 3 ingredients in the ratio $x : 3 : 2x$. $450\,\text{m}l$ is made. To make this amount $150\,\text{m}l$ of the second ingredient is required.
(a) Find the ratio of the 3 ingredients.
(b) How much of the 3rd ingredient is required?

11 A quantity of chicken feed will feed 12 chickens for eight days. How long would the same quantity of chicken feed last fifteen chickens to the nearest day?

12 $8\,\text{kg}$ of apples cost £4.80. How much will $5\,\text{kg}$ of apples cost?

Summary of key points

- To find a percentage of a quantity change the percentage into a decimal and multiply it by the quantity.

- If an amount is increased by $x\%$ the new amount is $(100 + x)\%$ of the original amount.

- If an amount is decreased by $x\%$ the new amount is $(100 - x)\%$ of the original amount.

- When a quantity changes (increases or decreases) find the percentage change using

$$\text{percentage change} = \frac{\text{actual change}}{\text{original quantity}} \times 100\%$$

- Compound interest is interest paid on an amount and on the interest on that amount.

- You can use ratios to show how things are divided or shared.

- Two quantities are in direct proportion if their ratio stays the same as the quantities increase or decrease.

- Two quantities are in inverse proportion when one increases at the same rate as the other decreases.

3 Equations

3.1 Solving simple equations

- To rearrange an equation you can
  - add the same quantity to both sides
  - subtract the same quantity from both sides
  - multiply both sides by the same quantity
  - divide both sides by the same quantity.
- Whatever you do to one side of an equation you must do to the other side. This is called the *balance* method.

Example 1

Solve the equation $5x - 2 = 12$ using the balance method.

$$5x - 2 = 12$$
Add 2 to both sides: $\quad 5x = 12 + 2$
$$5x = 14$$
Divide both sides by 5: $\quad x = 2\frac{4}{5}$

> You can think of the -2 on the left-hand side moving to the right-hand side and becoming $+2$.

Example 2

Solve the equation $3(x + 4) = 10$ using the balance method.

$$3(x + 4) = 10$$
Expand the brackets: $\quad 3x + 12 = 10$
Subtract 12 from both sides: $\quad 3x = 10 - 12$
$$3x = -2$$
Divide both sides by 3: $\quad x = -\frac{2}{3}$

> Alternative method for solving $3(x + 4) = 10$:
> Divide both sides by 3:
> $$x + 4 = 3\frac{1}{3}$$
> Subtract 4 from both sides:
> $$x = 3\frac{1}{3} - 4 = -\frac{2}{3}$$

- The *inverse* of an operation is the opposite operation.
- You can solve some types of equation using inverse operations.

> $+4$ is the inverse of -4.
> $\times 5$ is the inverse of $\div 5$.

Example 3

Solve the equation $5x - 2 = 12$ using inverse operations.

Use a flow diagram to show the operations needed to build the expression $5x - 2$:

$$x \xrightarrow{\times 5} 5x \xrightarrow{-2} 5x - 2$$

As this is equal to 12, you can start at the right-hand side and use a flow diagram with the inverse operations to find the value of x:

$$2\frac{4}{5} \xleftarrow{\div 5} 14 \xleftarrow{+2} 12$$

$$x = 2\frac{4}{5}$$

Example 4

Solve the equation $3(x + 4) = 10$ using inverse operations.

$$x \xrightarrow{\;+4\;} x + 4 \xrightarrow{\;\times 3\;} 3(x + 4)$$

$$-\tfrac{2}{3} \xleftarrow{\;-4\;} 3\tfrac{1}{3} \xleftarrow{\;\div 3\;} 10$$

$$x = -\tfrac{2}{3}$$

■ **You can solve most linear equations using the balance method, including any which can be solved using inverse operations.**

Exercise 3A	Links (*2A, 2D, 10E*)

Solve these equations:

1 $4x + 5 = 17$ **2** $3x - 5 = 16$ **3** $5(x + 2) = 40$ **4** $7(x - 4) = 21$

5 $\dfrac{x - 4}{6} = 2$ **6** $\dfrac{x}{4} + 6 = 11$ **7** $9x - 1 = 2$ **8** $3(x + 5) = 6$

9 $2x + 3 = 10$ **10** $5(x + 2) = 10$ **11** $\dfrac{x}{3} + 6 = 2$ **12** $3x + 7 = 2$

13 $4(x - 1) = 7$ **14** $\dfrac{x + 10}{6} = 1$ **15** $8x + 9 = 9$ **16** $\dfrac{x}{3} - 1 = 5$

17 $2(3x - 1) = 3$ **18** $\dfrac{4x - 3}{5} = 2$ **19** $\dfrac{2x}{3} + 5 = 1$ **20** $\dfrac{3(x + 4)}{2} = 5$

3.2 Equations with the unknown on both sides

■ **You can use the balance method to solve equations with the unknown on both sides.**

Example 5

Solve the equation $8x - 1 = 3x + 2$.

$$8x - 1 = 3x + 2$$
Subtract $3x$ from both sides: $8x - 3x - 1 = 2$
Collect like terms: $5x - 1 = 2$
Add 1 to both sides: $5x = 2 + 1$
$$5x = 3$$
Divide both sides by 5: $x = \tfrac{3}{5}$

Example 6

Solve the equation $7x + 9 = 4(x - 3)$ using the balance method.

$$7x + 9 = 4(x - 3)$$
Expand brackets: $7x + 9 = 4x - 12$
Subtract $4x$ from both sides: $7x - 4x + 9 = -12$
Collect like terms: $3x + 9 = -12$

Subtract 9 from both sides:

$$3x = -12 - 9$$
$$3x = -21$$
$$x = -7$$

Exercise 3B   Links (*2B, 2D, 10E*) 2B, 10E

Solve these equations:

1 $4x - 3 = 3x + 2$

2 $x - 1 = 7x - 4$

3 $7(x - 3) = 2x + 9$

4 $5(x + 2) = 3(x + 8)$

5 $3x - 8 = 5x - 2$

6 $8x + 5 = 5(x + 1)$

7 $5(x - 2) = 2x + 3$

8 $9(x + 3) = 5(x + 6)$

9 $3(x + 2) + 4(x - 5) = 5x + 3$

10 $8x + 7 - 5(x + 2) = x - 7$

11 $3x - 2 + (2x - 1) = 8x - 1$

12 $6(x + 3) - (2x - 7) = 7x + 1$

13 $3(4x + 9) + 4(2x - 1) = 6(4x + 7)$

14 $5(4x - 3) + 3(2 - 5x) = 8x$

15 $7(3x + 4) - 3(4x - 5) = 7 + 6(5x - 1)$

3.3 Equations with negative coefficients

■ The coefficient is the number in front of the unknown.

■ You can use the balance method to solve linear equations with negative coefficients.

Teaching reference:
(*pp 19–21, section 2.1*)

In $4 - 3x$ the coefficient of x is -3.

Example 7

Solve the equation $5 - 4x = 17$.

$$5 - 4x = 17$$

Add $4x$ to both sides: $5 = 4x + 17$

Subtract 17 from both sides: $4x = -12$

Divide both sides by 4: $x = -3$

Alternative method:
Subtract 5 from both sides:
$$-4x = 12$$
Divide both sides by -4:
$$x = -3$$

Example 8

Solve the equation $5x + 2 = 7 - 4x$.

$$5x + 2 = 7 - 4x$$

Add $4x$ to both sides: $9x + 2 = 7$

Subtract 2 from both sides: $9x = 5$

Divide both sides by 9: $x = \frac{5}{9}$

You could subtract $5x$ from both sides:
$$2 = 7 - 9x$$
but positive coefficients are easier to work with.

Example 9

Solve the equation $13 - 4x = 1 - 9x$.

$$13 - 4x = 1 - 9x$$

Add $9x$ to both sides: $5x + 13 = 1$

Subtract 13 from both sides: $5x = -12$

Divide both sides by 5: $x = -2\frac{2}{5}$

You could add $4x$ to both sides:
$$13 = 1 - 5x$$
but it is safer to get rid of negative coefficients.

Exercise 3C
Links (*2C, 2E*) 2E, 2F

Solve these equations:

1 $11 - 3x = 5$ **2** $7 - 5x = 22$

3 $13 - 3x = x$ **4** $8 - 7x = 3x$

5 $4(5 - 3x) = 5$ **6** $3(1 - 2x) = 4x$

7 $4x + 9 = 13 - 2x$ **8** $9x + 10 = 3 - x$

9 $3(x - 4) = 8 - 5x$ **10** $6(x + 3) = 3 - 4x$

11 $4x - 7 = 2(7 - 4x)$ **12** $2x + 5 = 3(1 - 2x)$

13 $4(3 - 2x) = x$ **14** $5(1 - 4x) = 2(x + 8)$

15 $3(7x + 4) = 4(3 - 5x)$ **16** $8 - 3x = 2(1 - x)$

17 $5(3 - 2x) = 8 - 5x$ **18** $4(3 - 5x) = 3(6 - 7x)$

19 $3(4x + 1) - 5(3x - 2) = 9 - 7x$

20 $4(2 - 3x) - 3(x - 1) = 5(3 - 2x)$

3.4 Using equations to solve problems

Teaching reference:
pp 23–25, section 2.2

■ **You can use equations to solve problems.**

Example 10

I thought of a number. I multiplied it by 2 and subtracted 19 from the result. The answer was the same as when I multiplied the number by 3 and subtracted the result from 71.
What number did I think of?

Let x stand for the number.

Then

$$2x - 19 = 71 - 3x$$
$$5x - 19 = 71$$
$$5x = 90$$
$$x = 18$$

The number was 18.

Example 11

The length of a rectangle is $x + 8$ centimetres and its width is $2x - 7$ centimetres. The perimeter of the rectangle is 56 cm.

Find its width.

$$2(x + 8) + 2(2x - 7) = 56$$
$$2x + 16 + 4x - 14 = 56$$
$$6x + 2 = 56$$
$$6x = 54$$
$$x = 9$$

The width of the rectangle $= 2 \times 9 - 7 = 11$ cm.

Exercise 3D   Links (*2G, 10F*) 2G, 10F

1

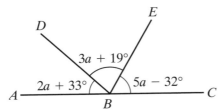

In the diagram, ABC is a straight line. Find the size of angle DBE.

2

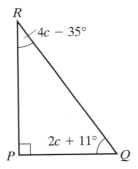

In the diagram, triangle PQR is right-angled at P.
Find the size of angle PQR.

3 The sizes of the angles of a quadrilateral are $x + 38°$, $x + 46°$, $x - 31°$ and $x - 9°$. Find the size of the smallest angle.

4 The lengths, in centimetres, of the sides of a triangle are $3d + 1$, $7d - 18$ and $41 - 2d$. Its perimeter is 64 cm. Find the lengths of its sides.

5 I multiply a number by 3 and add 4 to the result. The answer is the same as when I multiply the number by 5 and subtract 44 from the result. Find the number.

6 The length of each side of a square is $3y - 2$ centimetres. The perimeter of the square is 94 cm. Find the value of y.

7 $5x + 8$, $29 - 4x$ and $3x - 4$ are three numbers. Their mean is 19. Find the numbers.

8   Rashid is 34 years older than his daughter. He is also 3 times as old as she is. Find Rashid's age.

9   The width of a rectangle is 5 cm less than its length. The perimeter of the rectangle is 58 cm. Find its length.

10   I multiply a number by 3 and subtract the result from 49. The answer is the same as when I multiply the number by 5 and subtract the result from 75. Find the number.

11   The sum of two numbers is 46. Their difference is 12. Find the numbers.

12   The sum of the present ages of Mrs Banerji and her daughter is 55 years. Five years ago, Mrs Banerji was 4 times as old as her daughter. Find Mrs Banerji's present age.

13   Ffion has 26 coins in her purse. Some of them are 10p coins and the rest are 20p coins. Their total value is £4. Find the number of 20p coins in her purse.

14

$$5x - 7$$

$$4y - 13 \qquad\qquad\qquad 29 - 2y$$

$$2x + 17$$

The diagram shows a rectangle. Find the values of x and y.

15   The sum of three consecutive *odd* numbers is 93. Find the largest of these numbers.

3.5 Equations with fractions

■   **To solve equations with algebraic fractions, first clear the denominators by multiplying both sides of the equation by the lowest common multiple of the denominators.**

Example 12

Solve the equation $\dfrac{4x + 3}{6} = \dfrac{x}{4} - 2$.

The lowest common multiple of 6 and 4 is 12.
So multiply both sides of the equation by 12.

$$12\left(\frac{4x + 3}{6}\right)$$

$$= \frac{12}{6}(4x + 3)$$

$$= 2(4x + 3)$$

$$= 8x + 6$$

$$\frac{4x + 3}{6} = \frac{x}{4} - 2$$

$$12\left(\frac{4x + 3}{6}\right) = 12\left(\frac{x}{4} - 2\right)$$

$$8x + 6 = 3x - 24$$

$$5x = -30$$

$$x = -6$$

$$12\left(\frac{x}{4} - 2\right)$$

$$= 12 \times \frac{x}{4} - 12 \times 2$$

$$= 3x - 24$$

Exercise 3E   **Links** *(2D)* **2D**

1 $\dfrac{x}{4} + 1 = \dfrac{x}{3}$ **2** $\dfrac{x}{3} - 3 = \dfrac{x}{6} + 1$

3 $\dfrac{x+2}{5} - 3 = 2$ **4** $\dfrac{x}{4} + \dfrac{x}{5} = 9$

5 $\dfrac{2x-7}{3} = 5$ **6** $\dfrac{5x}{8} - \dfrac{x}{4} = 1$

7 $\dfrac{8-3x}{4} = 5$ **8** $\dfrac{x}{8} + 5 = \dfrac{x+4}{2} - 6$

9 $\dfrac{9-4x}{2} = 5x - 6$ **10** $\dfrac{2x+5}{3} = \dfrac{3x-1}{4}$

11 $\dfrac{7-2x}{4} = \dfrac{2x}{3}$ **12** $\dfrac{4x+7}{3} = 1 - 2x$

13 $\dfrac{x+1}{2} = \dfrac{x-4}{5} + 2$ **14** $\dfrac{3x+1}{4} = \dfrac{4x-1}{8} + 2$

15 $\dfrac{4-7x}{4} = 3 - x$ **16** $2(x-5) = \dfrac{x}{3} + 1$

17 $\dfrac{7-4x}{3} = \dfrac{9-8x}{5}$ **18** $\dfrac{x+2}{3} + \dfrac{x-4}{5} = 2$

19 $\dfrac{2x}{5} + \dfrac{2x-1}{4} = 2$ **20** $3(x+4) = \dfrac{4x-3}{2} + 9$

21 $\dfrac{7x+2}{5} + \dfrac{3x-1}{10} = 2$ **22** $2(4x+1) = \dfrac{4x-5}{3} + 7$

23 $\dfrac{x}{3} - \dfrac{2x-9}{5} = 1$ **24** $\dfrac{x-1}{3} + 5 = \dfrac{x}{9} + 7$

25 $\dfrac{x+3}{5} - \dfrac{x+7}{6} = 1$ **26** $\dfrac{7-4x}{9} + \dfrac{4x-1}{6} = 2$

27 $\dfrac{x}{4} - \dfrac{2x-1}{3} = 2$ **28** $\dfrac{2x-1}{3} - \dfrac{3x-1}{4} = 1$

29 $1 - \dfrac{4x-3}{8} = \dfrac{5-6x}{4}$ **30** $\dfrac{x-1}{3} - \dfrac{x+6}{2} = \dfrac{x-6}{4}$

3.6 Quadratic equations

- A quadratic equation is one in which the highest power of x is x^2.

- You can solve some simple quadratic equations using inverse operations.

- The inverse operation of 'square' is 'find the square roots'.

- A quadratic equation usually has two solutions.

> $x^2 + 4 = 29$, $3x^2 - 6 = 42$ and $25x^2 = 9$ are quadratic equations.

> The square root of 36 can be 6 or −6 because
> $6 \times 6 = 36$ and
> $-6 \times -6 = 36$.

Example 13

Solve the quadratic equation $2x^2 - 7 = 43$.
Use a flow diagram to show the operations needed to build the expression $2x^2 - 7$:

$$x \xrightarrow{\text{square}} x^2 \xrightarrow{\times 2} 2x^2 \xrightarrow{-7} 2x^2 - 7$$

As this is equal to 43, you can start at the right-hand side and use a flow diagram with the inverse operations to find the value of x.

$$\pm 5 \xleftarrow[\text{roots}]{\text{find square}} 25 \xleftarrow{\div 2} 50 \xleftarrow{+7} 43$$

The solutions are $x = 5$ or $x = -5$, which is usually written as $x = \pm 5$.
Alternatively, you could show the steps like this:

$$2x^2 - 7 = 43$$

Add 7 to both sides: $\quad 2x^2 = 50$
Divide both sides by 2: $\quad x^2 = 25$
Find the square roots of both sides: $\quad x = \pm 5$

Example 14

Solve the quadratic equation $16x^2 = 9$.

$$x \xrightarrow{\text{square}} x^2 \xrightarrow{\times 16} 16x^2$$

$$\pm \tfrac{3}{4} \xleftarrow[\text{roots}]{\text{find square}} \tfrac{9}{16} \xleftarrow{\div 16} 9$$

$$x = \pm \tfrac{3}{4}$$

Exercise 3F

Solve these quadratic equations:

1 $x^2 + 5 = 41$ **2** $x^2 - 10 = 39$ **3** $5x^2 = 45$

4 $7x^2 = 28$ **5** $\dfrac{x^2}{5} = 20$ **6** $3x^2 + 8 = 20$

7 $2x^2 - 5 = 27$ **8** $x^2 = \frac{16}{25}$ **9** $x^2 = \frac{25}{16}$

10 $9x^2 = 1$ **11** $9x^2 = 25$ **12** $25x^2 = 9$

13 $9x^2 = 36$ **14** $81x^2 = 4$ **15** $25x^2 = 49$

16 $16x^2 = 100$ **17** $(x + 3)^2 = 49$ **18** $(x - 5)^2 = 81$

19 $4(x - 2)^2 = 36$ **20** $(x + 1)^2 - 7 = 57$

3.7 Equations with the unknown in the denominator

■ **You can use balancing to solve equations in which the unknown appears in the denominator.**

This means equations like $\dfrac{20}{x} = 4$ and $\dfrac{5}{3x} = 2$.

Example 15

Solve the equation $\dfrac{3}{x} = 5$.

$$\frac{3}{x} = 5$$

Multiply both sides by x: $3 = 5x$ ——————— $x \times \dfrac{3}{x} = 3$

Divide both sides by 5: $x = \frac{3}{5}$ cancel xs

Example 16

Solve the equation $\dfrac{15}{4x} = 2$.

$$\frac{15}{4x} = 2$$

Multiply both sides by x: $\dfrac{15}{4} = 2x$

Divide both sides by 2: $\dfrac{15}{8} = x$ ——————— $\dfrac{15}{4 \times 2} = \dfrac{15}{8}$

                                 cancel xs

$$x = 1\tfrac{7}{8}$$

Example 17

Solve the equation $\dfrac{2}{2x - 1} = 3$.

$$\frac{2}{2x - 1} = 3$$

Multiply both sides by $2x - 1$: $2 = 3(2x - 1)$ ———————

Expand brackets: $2 = 6x - 3$

Add 3 to both sides: $5 = 6x$

Divide both sides by 5: $x = \frac{5}{6}$

$2x - 1$ goes from the bottom on the left-hand side to the top on the right-hand side. This is sometimes called 'cross multiplying'.

Exercise 3G

Solve these equations:

1 $\dfrac{36}{x} = 4$ **2** $\dfrac{5}{x} = 8$ **3** $\dfrac{8}{x} = 5$

4 $\dfrac{1}{x} = 6$ **5** $\dfrac{3}{2x} = 5$ **6** $\dfrac{13}{3x} = 2$

7 $\dfrac{12}{5x} = 1$ **8** $\dfrac{1}{8x} = 3$ **9** $\dfrac{2}{x - 3} = 5$

10 $\dfrac{7}{x + 5} = 2$ **11** $\dfrac{1}{3x - 2} = 4$ **12** $\dfrac{3}{4x + 5} = 2$

13 $\dfrac{4}{2x-5}=3$ **14** $\dfrac{3}{2x+5}=1$ **15** $\dfrac{6}{3x-8}=1$

16 $\dfrac{7}{5x+7}=1$ **17** $\dfrac{3}{4-x}=2$ **18** $\dfrac{5}{1-x}=3$

19 $\dfrac{2}{3-4x}=1$ **20** $\dfrac{13}{3-2x}=3$

3.8 Trial and improvement

■ **You can use trial and improvement to solve an equation to any degree of accuracy by trying a value in the equation and changing it to bring the result closer and closer to the solution.**

Example 18

Find a positive solution to the equation $x^3 + 4x^2 = 32$. Give your answer correct to 1 decimal place.

x	$x^3 + 4x^2$	Greater or smaller than 32
1	5	smaller
2	24	smaller
3	63	greater
2.5	40.625	greater
2.1	26.901	smaller
2.2	30.008	smaller
2.3	33.327	greater
2.25	31.640 625	smaller

There is a solution in the range $2 \leqslant x \leqslant 3$.

There is a solution in the range $2 \leqslant x \leqslant 2.5$.

There is a solution in the range $2.2 \leqslant x \leqslant 2.3$.

There is a solution in the range $2.25 \leqslant x \leqslant 2.3$.

$x = 2.3$ (to 1 decimal place).

Note: the evaluation of $x^3 + 4x^2$ for $x = 2.25$ is a necessary part of the working.
Without it, you cannot be sure that the solution is closer to $x = 2.3$ than it is to $x = 2.2$.

Exercise 3H   **Links (*18F*) 18F**

In questions **1–8**, find the positive solution to each equation:

1 $x^3 + 5x = 30$ (1 d.p.)   **2** $x^3 - 3x^2 = 10$ (1 d.p.)

3 $x^3 - 2x = 2$ (2 d.p.)   **4** $x^3 + 5x^2 = 100$ (2 d.p.)

5 $x^3 + 3x - 20 = 0$ (2 d.p.)   **6** $x^3 - 2x^2 - 25 = 0$ (2 d.p.)

7 $x^2 - \dfrac{3}{x} = 20$ (2 d.p.)   **8** $x - \dfrac{5}{x^2} = 4$ (2 d.p.)

9 The equation $x^2 + \dfrac{3}{x} = 19$ has *two* positive solutions.

    (a) One of the solutions lies between 0 and 1. Find this solution correct to 3 decimal places.

    (b) Find the other solution correct to 2 decimal places.

10

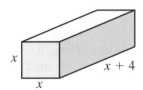

The diagram shows a prism which has a square as its cross-section. The length of each side of the square is x centimetres. The length of the prism is $x + 4$ centimetres. The volume of the prism is $200 \, \text{cm}^3$. Find the value of x. Give your answer correct to 2 decimal places.

Exercise 3I   Mixed questions

Solve the equations in questions **1–27**.

1 $3x + 7 = 15$ **2** $5x - 2 = 1$

3 $4(x - 5) = 3$ **4** $6(x + 3) = 11$

5 $\dfrac{2x + 7}{5} = 2$ **6** $7x + 4 = 3x - 8$

7 $4(3x - 2) = 7(x + 1)$ **8** $5x + 3 - (3x - 7) = x + 9$

9 $4(2x + 3) + 3(x - 5) = 6(x - 1)$ **10** $10 - 9x = 4$

11 $5 - 2x = 4x - 1$ **12** $8 - 3x = 6 - 7x$

13 $8x - 7 = 3(x - 1)$ **14** $5 + 3(3 - 2x) = 4x + 2(10 - 3x)$

15 $\dfrac{x}{3} + \dfrac{x}{4} - \dfrac{x}{6} = 2$ **16** $\dfrac{9 - 4x}{3} = 4$

17 $\dfrac{2x - 7}{5} = 3 - 4x$ **18** $\dfrac{3x + 7}{4} + \dfrac{2x - 5}{8} = 2x + 1$

19 $\dfrac{2(x - 1)}{3} - \dfrac{3(x - 2)}{4} = 1$ **20** $x^2 + 5 = 86$

21 $4x^2 - 17 = 83$ **22** $36x^2 = 25$

23 $4x^2 = 49$ **24** $\dfrac{5}{x} = 9$

25 $\dfrac{11}{2x} = 4$ **26** $\dfrac{4}{3x + 5} = 1$ **27** $\dfrac{11}{1 - 2x} = 2$

28 The size of each of the equal angles of an isosceles triangle is $x + 10°$. The size of the other angle is $98 - x°$. Find the size of each angle of the triangle.

29 I multiply a number by 3 and add 9 to the result. The answer is the same as when I multiply the number by 2 and subtract the result from 94. Find the number.

30 Solve these equations. Give your answers correct to 2 decimal places.

(a) $x^3 - 4x = 60$ **(b)** $x^3 + 3x^2 = 80$ **(c)** $x^2 - \dfrac{2}{x} = 11$

Summary of key points

■ **To rearrange an equation you can**
  • **add the same quantity to both sides**
  • **subtract the same quantity from both sides**
  • **multiply both sides by the same quantity**
  • **divide both sides by the same quantity.**

■ **Whatever you do to one side of an equation you must do to the other side. This is called the *balance* method.**

■ **The *inverse* of an operation is the opposite operation.**

■ **You can solve some types of equation using inverse operations.**

■ **You can solve most linear equations using the balance method, including any which can be solved using inverse operations.**

■ **You can use the balance method to solve equations with the unknown on both sides.**

■ **The coefficient is the number in front of the unknown.**

■ **You can use the balance method to solve linear equations with negative coefficients.**

■ **You can use equations to solve problems.**

■ **To solve equations with algebraic fractions, first clear the denominators by multiplying both sides of the equation by the lowest common multiple of the denominators.**

■ **A quadratic equation is one in which the highest power of x is x^2.**

■ **You can solve some simple quadratic equations using inverse operations.**

- The inverse operation of 'square' is 'find the square roots'.

- A quadratic equation usually has two solutions.

- You can use balancing to solve equations in which the unknown appears in the denominator.

- You can use trial and improvement to solve an equation to any degree of accuracy by trying a value in the equation and changing it to bring the result closer and closer to the solution.

4 Basic algebra to powers/ index laws

4.1 Expanding brackets

- To expand an expression, multiply each term inside the brackets by the term outside.
- A $-$ sign outside a bracket changes the sign of every term inside the brackets.

Example 1

Expand these expressions:

(a) $6(x + 4)$
(b) $-3(5x - 2)$
(c) $5x(2x - 7)$
(d) $(3x - 5)x$

(a) $6(x + 4) = 6x + 24$
(b) $-3(5x - 2) = -15x + 6$
(c) $5x(2x - 7) = 10x^2 - 35x$
(d) $(3x - 5)x = 3x^2 - 5x$

Exercise 4A **Links (10B) 10B**

Expand these expressions:

1 $4(x + 7)$	**2** $9(x - 2)$	**3** $5(4x + 1)$
4 $2(9x - 4)$	**5** $3(7 - 4x)$	**6** $x(x + 9)$
7 $x(x - 8)$	**8** $x(5x - 4)$	**9** $x(2x + 7)$
10 $x(3 - 2x)$	**11** $-2(x + 5)$	**12** $-7(4x - 1)$
13 $-5(6 - x)$	**14** $8x(2x + 7)$	**15** $7x(3x - 5)$
16 $4x(3 - 7x)$	**17** $-x(2x + 5)$	**18** $-9x(2x + 1)$
19 $-3x(5x - 4)$	**20** $-2x(8 + 3x)$	**21** $-4x(7 - x)$
22 $a(x + 5)$	**23** $a(3x - 7)$	**24** $5a(2x + 3)$
25 $7a(3x - 5)$	**26** $8a(a - 2x)$	**27** $(3x + 8)x$
28 $(7x - 5)x$	**29** $x^2(2x + 9)$	**30** $(5x - 4)x^2$

4.2 Factorizing

- Factorizing is the opposite of expanding.
- When an expression has been completely factorized, the terms inside the brackets do not have a common factor.

Teaching reference:
(*pp 187–188, section 10.3*)
pp 202–203, section 10.3

Example 2

Factorize these expressions completely:

(a) $5x + 35$
(b) $x^2 - 7x$
(c) $12x^2 + 20x$

(a) $5x + 35 = 5(x + 7)$
(b) $x^2 - 7x = x(x - 7)$
(c) $12x^2 + 20x = 4x(3x + 5)$

$12x^2 + 20x = 4(3x^2 + 5x)$ and $12x^2 + 20x = x(12x + 20)$ but, in both cases, the terms inside the brackets have a common factor.

Exercise 4B   Links *(10C)* 10C

Factorize these expressions completely:

1 $6x + 18$		**2** $7x - 28$
3 $20x + 15$		**4** $16x - 24$
5 $ax + 8a$		**6** $ax - 5ab$
7 $14x^2 + 21$		**8** $27x^2 - 18$
9 $x^2 + x$		**10** $x^2 - 2x$
11 $8x^2 - 24x$		**12** $35x^2 + 21x$
13 $12x - 18x^2$		**14** $ax^2 - 4ax$
15 $4ax^2 + 20ax$		**16** $30ax^2 - 18ax$
17 $ax^2 - a^2x$		**18** $12a^2x + 8ax^2$
19 $15a - 20ax^2$		**20** $9a^2x - 21ax^2$

4.3 Simplifying expressions involving brackets

■ **You can simplify expressions by collecting like terms.**

Example 3

Expand and simplify these expressions:

(a) $5(x + 4) + (3x - 7)$
(b) $4(2x - 1) + 7(x + 3)$
(c) $4(3x + 1) - (7x - 2)$
(d) $9x - 2(3x - 4)$

(a) $5(x + 4) + (3x - 7) = 5x + 20 + 3x - 7 = 8x + 13$
(b) $4(2x - 1) + 7(x + 3) = 8x - 4 + 7x + 21 = 15x + 17$
(c) $4(3x + 1) - (7x - 2) = 12x + 4 - 7x + 2 = 5x + 6$
(d) $9x - 2(3x - 4) = 9x - 6x + 8 = 3x + 8$

$+(3x - 7)$ means $+1(3x - 7)$
$= +3x - 7$

If there is just a $+$ sign outside the brackets, you remove the brackets.

Exercise 4C   Links (*10D*) 10D

Expand and simplify these expressions:

1 $4(x + 2) + (x - 9)$

2 $6x - 5 + (3x + 2)$

3 $3(2x - 5) + 2(x + 4)$

4 $5(2x + 3) + 4(2x - 7)$

5 $8 + 3(2x - 5)$

6 $5x - (x + 9)$

7 $7x - (3x - 1)$

8 $8 - (5x + 2)$

9 $6(2x - 5) - 5(x + 3)$

10 $4(3x + 2) - 3(2x - 7)$

11 $8(x + 1) - 4(2x - 3)$

12 $7x - (7x - 9)$

13 $9 - 4(2x + 5)$

14 $11x - 4(3x - 5)$

15 $7x + 12 - 3(x + 4)$

16 $9x - 4(2x - 3) + 1$

17 $x(x - 2) + 5(x - 3)$

18 $x(x + 4) - 7(x - 3)$

19 $x(3x - 4) + 6(2x - 1)$

20 $x(7x - 4) - 2(3x + 5)$

21 $3x(2x - 1) + 4(2x - 1)$

22 $2x(5x + 3) - 5(2x + 3)$

23 $7(x - 1) + 4(x + 5) - 6(x + 3)$

24 $5(2x + 5) - 4(3x - 1) + 2(x - 8)$

25 $12 + 3(4x - 5) - (7x + 8)$

26 $9x - 4(3 - 2x) + 7$

27 $3x - (4x - 9) + 5(2x + 1)$

28 $7(x - 4) + 5 - 3(2x - 1)$

29 $9x + (5x - 4) - 3(4x - 5) - 9$

30 $10 + 3(x - 5) - 5(2x - 1) + 7x$

4.4 Indices

■ **In the expression x^n, the number n is called the *index* or *power*.**

■ **These are the laws of indices:**

- $x^m \times x^n = x^{m+n}$
- $x^m \div x^n = x^{m-n}$
- $(x^m)^n = x^{mn}$

> Teaching reference:
> (*pp 356–358, sections 20.1, 20.2, 20.3*)
> pp 407–410, sections 20.1, 20.2

> The plural of 'index' is 'indices'.

Example 4

Simplify these expressions:

(a) $3x^2y^3 \times 5x^4y$ (b) $20x^6y^4 \div 4x^2y^3$ (c) $(2x^4)^3$

(a) $3x^2y^3 \times 5x^4y = 3 \times x^2 \times y^3 \times 5 \times x^4 \times y^1$
$= 3 \times 5 \times x^2 \times x^4 \times y^3 \times y^1$
$= 15 \times x^{2+4}y^{3+1}$
$= 15x^6y^4$

(b) $20x^6y^4 \div 4x^2y^3 = \frac{20}{4}x^{6-2}y^{4-3}$
$= 5x^4y^1$
$= 5x^4y$

(c) $(2x^4)^3 = 2^3 \times (x^4)^3$
$= 8 \times x^{3 \times 4}$
$= 8x^{12}$

> Alternatively, you can write $20x^6y^4 \div 4x^2y^3$ as $\frac{20x^6y^4}{4x^2y^3}$ and then cancel.

Exercise 4D   **Links (*20A*, *20B*) 20A, 20B**

Simplify these expressions:

1. $x^2 \times x^7$
2. $x^7 \div x^4$
3. $(x^5)^2$
4. $2x^3 \times 7x^5$
5. $5x \times 8x^5$
6. $2x^5 \times 5x^6 \times 3x^2$
7. $18x^8 \div 3x^5$
8. $20x^6 \div 4x^5$
9. $24x^6 \div 6x$
10. $(3x^2)^4$
11. $(4x)^3$
12. $7x^4 y^3 \times 3x^2 y^4$
13. $5x^6 \times 4x^3 y^5$
14. $8xy^4 \times 7x^7 y^2$
15. $3x^4 y^2 \times 2x^3 y^5 \times 5x^2 y$
16. $28x^7 y^5 \div 4x^4 y^2$
17. $36x^6 y^8 \div 12x^2 y$
18. $15x^9 \div 25x^4$
19. $20x^5 y^3 \div 5x^2 y^3$
20. $5x^4 \times (4x^3)^2$
21. $(4x^4 y^5)^2$
22. $(2x^4 y^2)^3 \times 5x$
23. $\dfrac{6x^5 \times 4x^3}{8x^6}$
24. $\dfrac{9x^5 \times 4x^6}{6x^3 \times 3x^4}$
25. $\dfrac{6x^3 y^5 \times 8x^9 y^4}{2xy \times 3x^5 y^6}$

4.5 The zero index and negative indices

Teaching reference:
(*pp 359–361, section 20.3*)
pp 410–411, section 20.3

- $x^0 = 1$ for all non-zero values of x.

- $x^{-n} = \dfrac{1}{x^n}$

Example 5

(a) Evaluate (i) $7a^0$ (ii) $\dfrac{15x^3}{5x^3}$

(b) Copy and complete (i) $\dfrac{1}{x^6} = x^?$ (ii) $x^{-4} = \dfrac{1}{x^?}$

(a) (i) $7a^0 = 7 \times 1 = 7$

    (ii) $\dfrac{15x^3}{5x^3} = \dfrac{15}{5} x^{3-3} = 3x^0 = 3$

Alternatively, you can cancel by x^3.

(b) (i) $\dfrac{1}{x^6} = x^{-6}$

    (ii) $x^{-4} = \dfrac{1}{x^4}$

Example 6

Use the laws of indices to simplify these expressions:

(a) $\dfrac{6x^3}{2x^5}$

(b) $(x^{-2})^5$

(c) $(x^{-3})^{-4}$

(a) $\dfrac{6x^3}{2x^5} = \dfrac{6}{2} x^{3-5} = 3x^{-2}$

You can write $3x^{-2}$ as $\dfrac{3}{x^2}$.

(b) $(x^{-2})^5 = x^{-2 \times 5} = x^{-10}$

(c) $(x^{-3})^{-4} = x^{-3 \times -4} = x^{12}$

Exercise 4E

1 Evaluate

    (a) $9x^0$ **(b)** $\dfrac{18x^5}{12x^5}$ **(c)** $\dfrac{x^4}{2x^4}$ **(d)** $(4x)^0$ **(e)** $4 \times x^0$

2 Copy and complete

    (a) $\dfrac{1}{x^3} = x^?$ **(b)** $x^{-8} = \dfrac{1}{x^?}$

3 Use the laws of indices to simplify these expressions:

    (a) $x^5 \times x^{-8}$ **(b)** $x^{-2} \times x^{-3}$ **(c)** $4x^{-5} \times 5x^7$

    (d) $x^5 \div x^8$ **(e)** $x^{-2} \div x^3$ **(f)** $x^2 \div x^{-4}$

    (g) $20x \div 5x^4$ **(h)** $\dfrac{24x^5}{3x^8}$ **(i)** $(x^{-2})^4$

    (j) $(x^{-3})^{-5}$ **(k)** $(3x^4)^{-2}$ **(l)** $\dfrac{x^5 y^4}{x^2 y^7}$

4.6 Expressions, equations, formulae and identities

- In algebra, an **expression** is a combination of letters and numbers.

         For example, $2a + 3b$ and $5n - 3$ are expressions.

- An **equation** is a mathematical statement that two expressions are equal. Sometimes a letter denotes a missing number.

         For example, $4 + 5 = 9$, $y = 3x - 1$ and $2(x + 3) = 16$ are equations.

- A **formula** is a quick way of expressing a rule.

         For example, $C = \pi d$ and $P = 2l + 2b$ are formulae.

- An **identity** is an equation which is true for all values of the letter.

         For example, $3x + 4x = 7x$ and $5(x - 3) = 5x - 15$ are identities.

Example 7

Cinema tickets cost £5 for adults and £3 for children. Write down an expression for the total cost, in pounds, of cinema tickets for a adults and c children.

$5a + 3c$ is an expression for the total cost.

         There are many other possible expressions, such as $a + a + a + a + a + c + c + c$, but you should always write expressions as simply as possible.

Example 8

The lengths, in centimetres, of the sides of an isosceles triangle are a, a and b. Write down a formula for the perimeter, P, of the triangle.

    $P = 2a + b$

         Formulae always have an equals sign but expressions do not.

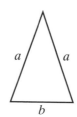

Example 9

Some of these equations are true for a particular value of x and the rest are true for all values of x, i.e. they are identities. For each equation, either solve the equation or explain why it is an identity.

(a) $3x + 4 + 2x - 1 = 5x + 3$ (b) $5x + 4 - 3x = x + 7$

(c) $5(x + 2) = 5x + 10$ (d) $5(x - 2) = 2x + 11$

(a) When you simplify $3x + 4 + 2x - 1$, you get $5x + 3$ and so $3x + 4 + 2x - 1 = 5x + 3$ is an identity.

(b)
$$5x + 4 - 3x = x + 7$$
Simplify the left-hand side: $2x + 4 = x + 7$

Subtract x from both sides: $x + 4 = 7$

Subtract 4 from both sides: $x = 3$

(c) When you expand $5(x + 2)$, you get $5x + 10$ and so $5(x + 2) = 5x + 10$ is an identity.

(d)
$$5(x - 2) = 2x + 11$$
Expand the brackets: $5x - 10 = 2x + 11$

Subtract $2x$ from both sides: $3x - 10 = 11$

Add 10 to both sides: $3x = 21$

Divide both sides by 3: $x = 7$

Exercise 4F

1 Write down an expression for the number of days in n weeks.

2 The length of each side of a regular pentagon is a centimetres. Write down an expression for its perimeter.

3 There are 56 seats in a first-class railway carriage and 64 seats in a standard-class carriage. Write down an expression for the total number of seats on a train with f first-class carriages and g standard-class carriages.

4 The sum of two numbers is 25. One of the numbers is n. Write down an expression for the other number.

5 The product of two numbers is 36. One of the numbers is y. Write down an expression for the other number.

6 The length of each side of a regular hexagon is h centimetres. Write down a formula for the perimeter, P, of the hexagon.

7 A motorist travels d miles in t hours. Write down a formula for the average speed, v miles per hour.

8 Write down a formula for the area, A, of a triangle in terms of its base, b, and its vertical height, h.

9 Cartons of orange juice cost 47p each. Pat bought n cartons and paid for them with a £5 note. Write down a formula for the change, C pence, she should have received.

10 Some of these equations are true for a particular value of x and the rest are true for all values of x, i.e. they are identities. For each equation, either solve the equation or explain why it is an identity.

(a) $6x - 1 + 2x = 5x + 14$
(b) $7x + 2 - 3x - 5 = 4x - 3$
(c) $7(x - 3) = 7x - 21$
(d) $6(x + 2) = x - 3$
(e) $6(x - 5) = 3(2x - 10)$
(f) $6(x - 5) = 3x$
(g) $5(x - 1) - 3(x - 2) = 4x - 5$
(h) $5(x - 1) - 3(x - 2) = 2x + 1$
(i) $7x - 2x = 5x$
(j) $7x - 2x = 4x$

Exercise 4G   Mixed questions

1 Expand these expressions:
(a) $8(x + 5)$
(b) $7(3x - 4)$
(c) $5(1 - 6x)$
(d) $x(9x - 2)$
(e) $-4(2x + 5)$
(f) $6x(x - 3)$
(g) $-2x(5x - 7)$
(h) $a(8x + 3a)$
(i) $(9 - 4x)x$

2 Factorize these expressions completely:
(a) $9x - 27$
(b) $28x + 21$
(c) $10x^2 - 20$
(d) $x^2 - x$
(e) $32x^2 + 40x$
(f) $24x + 16x^2$
(g) $ax^2 - bx$
(h) $6ax^2 - 9ax$
(i) $25ax - 15ax^2$

3 Expand and simplify these expressions:
(a) $7(x - 3) + (2x - 1)$
(b) $6(2x + 3) + 5(3x - 4)$
(c) $4(3x - 5) - (7x - 9)$
(d) $2(7x + 4) - 3(2x + 1)$
(e) $9 - 5(3x - 2)$
(f) $11x + 5(2 - 3x)$
(g) $x(x + 9) - 4(x - 2)$
(h) $6(2 - 3x) + 5 - 8(1 - 2x)$

4 Simplify these expressions:
(a) $x^5 \times x^3$
(b) $x^9 \div x^4$
(c) $(x^3)^5$
(d) $3x^4 \times 2x^6$
(e) $32x^7 \div 4x^2$
(f) $(2x^3)^5$
(g) $5x^4 y^3 \times 4x^5 y^2$
(h) $40x^6 y^4 \div 5x^5 y^4$
(i) $\dfrac{9x^3 \times 2x^8}{6x^7}$

5 Evaluate
(a) y^0
(b) $3y^0$
(c) $(3y)^0$

6 Use the laws of indices to simplify these expressions:
(a) $x^{-4} \times x^3$
(b) $3x^{-4} \times 5x^{-5}$
(c) $x^2 \div x^6$
(d) $18x^2 \div 6x^{-3}$
(e) $\dfrac{27x^4}{9x^9}$
(f) $(x^3)^{-2}$
(g) $(x^{-2})^{-6}$
(h) $(2x^5)^{-3}$

7 The two equal angles of an isosceles triangle are each $a°$. Write down an expression for the size, in degrees, of the other angle.

8 The length of each side of a cube is d centimetres. The total surface area of the cube is A cm². Write down a formula for A in terms of d.

9 State which of these equations are identities and solve the remaining equations:

(a) $5x + 3x = 8x$

(b) $8(x + 4) = 8x + 32$

(c) $5x + 3x = 2(x + 12)$

(d) $3(2x - 5) + 4(3x - 1) = 19x - 18$

(e) $6(6x - 4) = 4(9x - 6)$

(f) $3(2x - 1) - 2(3x - 2) = 1$

10 Investigate these equations:

(a) $5x + 3x = 8x + 1$

(b) $8(x + 4) = 8x + 30$

Summary of key points

■ **To expand an expression, multiply each term inside the brackets by the term outside.**

■ **A − sign outside a bracket changes the sign of every term inside the brackets.**

■ **Factorizing is the opposite of expanding.**

■ **When an expression has been completely factorized, the terms inside the brackets do not have a common factor.**

■ **You can simplify expressions by collecting like terms.**

■ **In the expression x^n, the number n is called the *index* or *power*.**

■ **These are the laws of indices:**

- $x^m \times x^n = x^{m+n}$
- $x^m \div x^n = x^{m-n}$
- $(x^m)^n = x^{mn}$

■ **$x^0 = 1$ for all non-zero values of x.**

■ **$x^{-n} = \dfrac{1}{x^n}$**

■ **In algebra, an expression is a combination of letters and numbers.**

■ **An equation is a mathematical statement that two expressions are equal. Sometimes a letter denotes a missing number.**

■ **A formula is a quick way of expressing a rule.**

■ **An identity is an equation which is true for all values of the letter.**

5 Sequences and formulae

- A sequence is a succession of numbers formed according to a rule.
- The numbers in a sequence are called the *terms* of the sequence.

5.1 Common sequences

- You should recognize these common sequences:
  - even numbers   2, 4, 6, 8, 10, 12, ...
  - odd numbers   1, 3, 5, 7, 9, 11, ...
  - square numbers   1, 4, 9, 16, 25, 36, ...
  - triangular numbers   1, 3, 6, 10, 15, 21, ...
  - cube numbers   1, 8, 27, 64, 125, ...
  - powers, e.g. powers of 2   2, 4, 8, 16, 32, 64, ...
  - multiples, e.g. multiples of 3   3, 6, 9, 12, 15, 18, ...

Most of these are covered in Chapter 1 of Edexcel GCSE Mathematics Higher Course.

$2^1 = 2$, $2^2 = 4$, $2^3 = 8$, etc.

Example 1

A marble is placed at the top of a maze and allowed to roll down. The diagram shows part of the maze and the number of different routes by which the marble can reach each junction on the first three rows of the maze. This pattern of numbers is called Pascal's triangle.

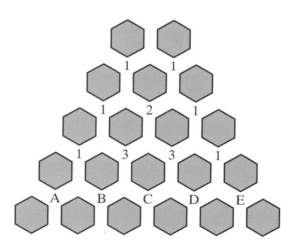

(a) Find the number of different routes to the junctions on the fourth row of the maze. Explain how you found them.
(b) Write down the first five rows of Pascal's triangle and give the mathematical names of any sequences you see.
(c) Find the sum of each of the first five rows of Pascal's triangle and give the mathematical name of the numbers you obtain.

(a) There is only one route to each of A and E, the junctions at the ends of the row.
To reach B, the marble must drop from one of the two junctions above B on the preceding row. So there are $1 + 3 = 4$ different routes to B. Similarly, there are $3 + 3 = 6$ different routes to C and $1 + 3 = 4$ different routes to D.

(b)
```
        1    1
     1    2    1
   1    3    3    1
 1    4    6    4    1
1    5   10   10   5    1
```

1, 2, 3, 4, 5, ... are natural numbers (also called counting numbers or positive integers).

1, 3, 6, 10, ... are triangular numbers.

(c) The sums of the first five rows are 2, 4, 8, 16 and 32. These numbers are powers of 2.

Exercise 5A   **Links (*9B*) 9B**

1 There are 2 possible outcomes when a coin is spun, 4 possible outcomes when two coins are spun and 8 possible outcomes when three coins are spun.

> See Example **5** in chapter 9 of Edexcel GCSE Mathematics Higher Course.

(a) Copy and complete the table to show the numbers of possible outcomes when 4, 5 and 6 coins are spun.

Number of coins	1	2	3	4	5	6
Number of possible outcomes	2	4	8			

(b) Calculate the number of possible outcomes when 10 coins are spun. Explain how you found your answer.

(c) Write down an expression, in terms of n, for the number of possible outcomes when n coins are spun.

2 Here are four patterns made with triangular tiles. Some of the tiles are grey and some are white.

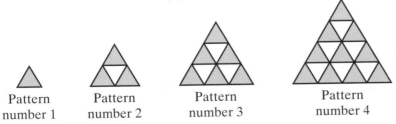

Pattern number 1   Pattern number 2   Pattern number 3   Pattern number 4

(a) Without drawing, find the number of grey tiles in pattern number 5. Explain how you found your answer.

(b) Without drawing, find the *total* number of tiles in pattern number 5. Explain how you found your answer.

(c) Write down an expression, in terms of *n*, for the total number of tiles in pattern number *n*.

(d) Find an expression, in terms of *n*, for
   (i) the number of grey tiles in pattern number *n*
   (ii) the number of white tiles in pattern number *n*.

(e) Write down the pattern number of the pattern in which the total number of tiles is 144.

5.2 The *n*th term of a sequence

■ When you know a formula for the *n*th term of a sequence, you can calculate any term of the sequence by substituting a value for *n* in the formula. *n* must be a positive integer ($n = 1, 2, 3, \ldots$).

■ Your syllabus only includes the *n*th terms of sequences in which the same number is added to or subtracted from a term to obtain the next term.

Teaching reference:
(*pp 253–256, sections 14.1, 14.2*)
pp 291–295, sections 14.1, 14.2

Such sequences are called *arithmetic* sequences.

Example 2

The *n*th term of a sequence is $5n - 2$. Find the first four terms.

Substituting $n = 1$, first term $= 5 \times \mathbf{1} - 2 = 5 - 2 = 3$
Substituting $n = 2$, second term $= 5 \times \mathbf{2} - 2 = 10 - 2 = 8$
Substituting $n = 3$, third term $= 5 \times \mathbf{3} - 2 = 15 - 2 = 13$
Substituting $n = 4$, fourth term $= 5 \times \mathbf{4} - 2 = 20 - 2 = 18$

The first four terms are 3, 8, 13, 18.

The differences are all 5, the same as the coefficient of *n* in the *n*th term.

Example 3

The first five terms of a sequence are 11, 7, 3, −1, −5.
Find an expression for the *n*th term of the sequence.

The differences are all 4 and the terms are decreasing.
So the *n*th term will include $-4n$ but an *n*th term of $-4n$ gives the sequence

   $-4, -8, -12, -16, -20 \ldots$

To obtain the required sequence, 15 must be added to each term and so the *n*th term is $15 - 4n$.

Exercise 5B   Links (*14A, 14C*) 14A, 14C

1 For sequences with these *n*th terms, find
   (a) the first five terms in the sequence,
   (b) the twelfth term of the sequence.

   (i) $6n$ **(ii)** $3n + 2$ **(iii)** $7n - 3$
   (iv) $32 - 5n$ **(v)** $24 - 8n$

2   Here are the first five terms of some sequences.
Find an expression for the *n*th term of each of the sequences:
(a)   7, 14, 21, 28, 35, ...   (b)   11, 17, 23, 29, 35, ...
(c)   7, 8, 9, 10, 11, ...   (d)   23, 19, 15, 11, 7, ...
(e)   5, 13, 21, 29, 37, ...   (f)   12, 11, 10, 9, 8, ...
(g)   31, 21, 11, 1, −9, ...   (h)   −14, −7, 0, 7, 14, ...

3   Find an expression for the *n*th term of each of these
sequences:
(a)   even numbers starting with 2
(b)   odd numbers starting with 1
(c)   multiples of 8 starting with 8
(d)   even numbers starting with 10
(e)   odd numbers starting with 15
(f)   multiples of 5 starting with 35.

5.3 Sequences of shapes

Teaching reference:
(*pp 253–256, sections 14.1,
14.2*)
pp 291–295, sections 14.1,
14.2

Example 4

Here are the first four shapes in a sequence made from
matchsticks:

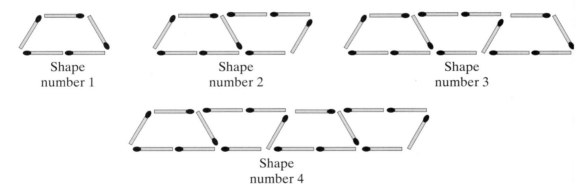

The table shows the number of matchsticks in each of these shapes:

Shape number (*n*)	1	2	3	4
Number of matchsticks	5	9	13	17

(a)   Work out the number of matchsticks in shape number 5 and in
      shape number 6.
(b)   find an expression for the number of matchsticks in shape
      number *n*.
(c)   Find the number of matchsticks in shape number 13.
(d)   Find the shape number of the shape with 77 matchsticks.

In other words, find the *n*th
term of the sequence 5, 9,
13, 17, ...

(a)   5   9   13   17
      differences   4   4   4
      In shape number 5, there are $17 + 4 = 21$ matchsticks.
      In shape number 6, there are $21 + 4 = 25$ matchsticks.

(b) The *n*th term will include $4n$ but an *n*th term of $4n$ gives the sequence 4, 8, 12, 16, 20, ...
To obtain the required sequence, 1 must be added to each term and so the *n*th term is $4n + 1$.

(c) Substituting $n = 13$ in $4n + 1$ gives the number of matchsticks in shape number 13.

$$\text{Number of matchsticks} = 4 \times 13 + 1 = 52 + 1 = 53$$

(d) To find the shape number of the shape with 77 matchsticks, solve the equation $4n + 1 = 77$.

$$4n + 1 = 77$$
Subtract 1 from both sides: $\quad 4n = 76$
Divide both sides by 4: $\quad n = 19$

Shape number 19 has 77 matchsticks.

Exercise 5C   Links (*14B, 14C*) 14B, 14C

1 Here are the first four shapes in four sequences of shapes made from matchsticks:

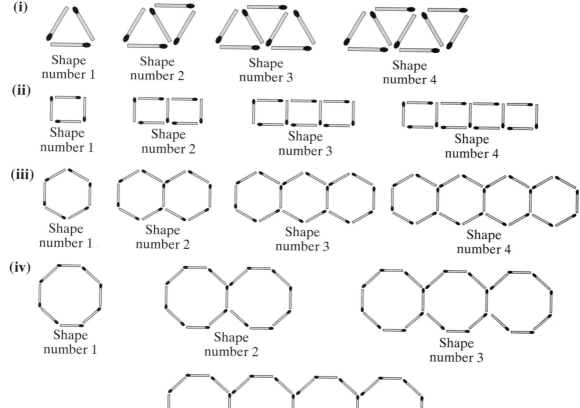

(i)

Shape number 1   Shape number 2   Shape number 3   Shape number 4

(ii)

Shape number 1   Shape number 2   Shape number 3   Shape number 4

(iii)

Shape number 1   Shape number 2   Shape number 3   Shape number 4

(iv)

Shape number 1   Shape number 2   Shape number 3

Shape number 4

For each sequence:
(a) work out the number of matchsticks in shape number 5 and in shape number 6,
(b) find an expression for the number of matchsticks in shape number n,
(c) find the number of matchsticks in shape number 30,
(d) find the shape number of the shape with 211 matchsticks.

2 (a) In question **1**, how is the coefficient of n in the expression for the number of matchsticks in shape number n related to the number of matchsticks in shape number 1? Explain why this is so.
(b) Write down an expression for the number of matchsticks in shape number n when the matchsticks in shape number 1 form a regular 20-sided polygon.

3 Here are four patterns made with square tiles:

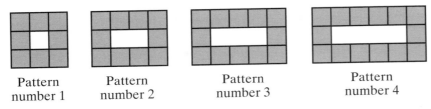

Pattern   Pattern   Pattern   Pattern
number 1   number 2   number 3   number 4

(a) Work out the number of tiles in pattern number 5 and in pattern number 6.
(b) Find an expression for the number of tiles in pattern number n.
(c) Find the number of tiles in pattern number 17.
(d) Find the pattern number of the pattern with 70 tiles.

4 Here are four patterns of dots:

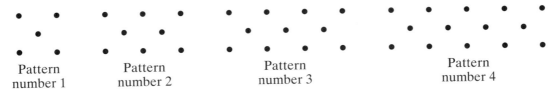

Pattern   Pattern   Pattern   Pattern
number 1   number 2   number 3   number 4

(a) Work out the number of dots in pattern number 5 and in pattern number 6.
(b) Find an expression for the number of dots in pattern number n.
(c) Find the number of dots in pattern number 29.
(d) Find the pattern number of the pattern with 110 dots.

5   Here are four patterns made with square tiles:

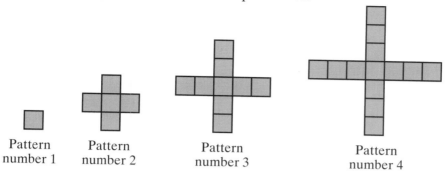

Pattern
number 1

Pattern
number 2

Pattern
number 3

Pattern
number 4

(a) Work out the number of tiles in pattern number 5 and in
     pattern number 6.
(b) Find an expression for the number of tiles in pattern
     number n.
(c) Find the number of tiles in pattern number 25.
(d) Find the pattern number of the pattern with 89 tiles.
(e) Find the pattern number of the largest pattern that can be
     made with 60 tiles.

6   Here are four patterns made with hexagonal tiles:

Pattern
number 1

Pattern
number 2

Pattern
number 3

Pattern
number 4

(a) Work out the number of tiles in pattern number 5 and in
     pattern number 6.
(b) Find an expression for the number of tiles in pattern
     number n.
(c) Find the number of tiles in pattern number 28.
(d) Find the pattern number of the pattern with 130 tiles.
(e) Find the pattern number of the largest pattern that can be
     made with 80 tiles.

5.4 Formulae

■ **A formula is a quick way of expressing a rule. It describes a
   relationship between two sets of numbers.**

Example 5

To find the sum, in degrees, of the interior angles of a polygon,
you subtract 2 from the number of sides and multiply the result
by 180.

(a) Write down a formula for the sum, $S°$, of the interior angles of
     an n-sided polygon.

(b) Write down a formula for the size, $i°$, of each interior angle of a *regular* n-sided polygon.

(a) $S = 180(n - 2)$

(b) $i = \dfrac{180(n - 2)}{n}$

■ **You can sometimes eliminate one of the letters from a formula by substituting for it an expression from a second formula.**

Example 6

$y = 5x - 2$ and $x = 2t + 1$.
Express y in terms of t.

$y = 5(2t + 1) - 2$
$y = 10t + 5 - 2$
$y = 10t + 3$

Exercise 5D   **Links 14G**

1 A motorist travels for t hours at an average speed of v miles per hour. Write down a formula for the distance, d miles, travelled.

2 To cook a joint of pork, you allow 30 minutes per pound and an extra 30 minutes. Write down a formula for the time, T minutes, needed to cook a joint of pork weighing W pounds.

3 The size of each exterior angle of a regular n-sided polygon is $e°$.
  (a) Write down a formula for e in terms of n.
  (b) Use your answer to part (a) to write down a formula for the size, $i°$, of each interior angle of a regular n-sided polygon.

Can you explain why the formula in **3(b)** and the one in part (b) of Example **5** are equivalent?

4 $T = kx$ and $E = \frac{1}{2}Tx$.
Find a formula for E in terms of k and x.

5 $V = \pi r^2 h$ and $S = 2\pi rh$.
Find a formula for V in terms of S and r.

6 The sum of the lengths of the edges of a cube is P centimetres. Find, in terms of P, a formula for (a) the total surface area, A cm^2, of the cube and (b) the volume, V cm^3, of the cube.

5.5 Evaluating formulae

■ **You need to be able to evaluate formulae by substituting values into them. This includes negative numbers and fractions.**

Example 7

$$s = ut - \tfrac{1}{2}gt^2$$

Calculate the value of s when $u = 24$, $g = 10$ and $t = 3$.

$$s = 24 \times 3 - \tfrac{1}{2} \times 10 \times 3^2$$
$$= 72 - 45$$
$$= 27$$

Exercise 5E   Links (14D) 14E

1 $y = 3x + 7$ Calculate the value of y when $x = -4$.

2 $V = IR$ Calculate the value of V when $I = 12$ and $R = 20$.

3 $A = \pi rl$ Calculate correct to 3 s.f. the value of A when $r = 7.3$ and $l = 9.1$.

4 $s = \dfrac{a + b + c}{2}$ Calculate the value of s when $a = 3.7$, $b = 4.2$ and $c = 5.3$.

5 $F = 1.8C + 32$ Calculate the value of F when $C = -40$.

6 $A = \tfrac{1}{2}(a + b)h$ Calculate the value of A when $a = 8$, $b = 7$ and $h = 5$.

7 $A = 4\pi r^2$ Calculate correct to 3 s.f. the value of A when $r = 7.3$.

8 $v = u - gt$ Calculate the value of v when $u = 7$, $g = 10$ and $t = 2$.

9 $d = \dfrac{C}{\pi}$ Calculate correct to 3 s.f. the value of d when $C = 16.8$.

10 $A = \dfrac{\pi d^2}{4}$ Calculate correct to 3 s.f. the value of A when $d = 8.7$.

11 $y = 3x^2 - 5$ Calculate the value of y when $x = -2$.

12 $s = \dfrac{(u + v)t}{2}$ Calculate the value of s when $u = 19$, $v = 35$ and $t = 2\tfrac{1}{2}$.

13 $d = v + \dfrac{v^2}{20}$ Calculate the value of d when $v = 41$.

14 $D = \tfrac{1}{2}n(n - 3)$ Calculate the value of D when $n = 12$.

15 $H = 17 - \dfrac{A}{2}$ Calculate the value of H when $A = 13$.

16 $E = \tfrac{1}{2}m(v^2 - u^2)$ Calculate the value of E when $m = 5$, $v = 7$ and $u = 10$.

17 $A = \pi(R + r)(R - r)$ Calculate correct to 3 s.f. the value of A when $R = 8.9$ and $r = 5.7$.

18 $y = \dfrac{10}{x-2}$ Calculate the value of y when $x = -\frac{1}{2}$.

19 $v = \dfrac{uf}{u-f}$ Calculate the value of v when $u = 3.4$ and $f = 26.52$.

20 $F = \dfrac{mv^2}{r}$ Calculate the value of F when $m = 9$, $v = 13$ and $r = 5$.

21 $V = \frac{4}{3}\pi r^3$ Calculate correct to 3 s.f. the value of V when $r = 14.3$.

22 $d = \dfrac{Wl^3}{3B}$ Calculate the value of d when $W = 18$, $l = 15$ and $B = 75$.

23 $P = 2l + \dfrac{100}{l}$ Calculate the value of P when $l = 8$.

24 $R = \dfrac{kl}{r^2}$ Calculate the value of R when $k = 0.00003$, $l = 280$ and $r = 2$.

25 $A = P\left(1 + \dfrac{R}{100}\right)^n$ Calculate the value of A when $P = 2000$, $R = 6\frac{1}{4}$ and $n = 2$.

26 $v = \sqrt{2gh}$ Calculate correct to 3 s.f. the value of v when $g = 9.81$ and $h = 23.8$.

27 $D = 5\sqrt{\dfrac{h}{2}}$ Calculate correct to 2 s.f. the value of D when $h = 19.7$.

28 $T = 2\pi\sqrt{\dfrac{I}{MH}}$ Calculate correct to 3 s.f. the value of T when $I = 125$, $M = 8$ and $H = 3$.

29 $v = \sqrt{u^2 + 2as}$ Calculate correct to 3 s.f. the value of v when $u = 20$, $a = -3$ and $s = 35$.

30 $v = \omega\sqrt{a^2 - x^2}$ Calculate the value of v when $\omega = 8$, $a = 29$ and $x = 21$.

5.6 Manipulating formulae

■ **To find the value of a letter which is not the subject of a formula, you substitute into the formula the values given and then solve the resulting equation.**

Example 8

$$s = ut - \tfrac{1}{2}gt^2$$

Calculate the value of u when $s = 39$, $g = 10$ and $t = 3$.

Substitute given values: $39 = u \times 3 - \frac{1}{2} \times 10 \times 3^2$

Simplify: $39 = 3u - 45$

Add 45 to both sides: $84 = 3u$

Divide both sides by 3: $u = 28$

1 $y = 3x + 7$ Calculate the value of x when $y = 1$.

2 $V = IR$ Calculate the value of R when $V = 240$ and $I = 5$.

3 $A = \pi r l$ Calculate correct to 3 s.f. the value of r when $A = 90$ and $l = 8.3$.

4 $s = \dfrac{a+b+c}{2}$ Calculate the value of a when $s = 12.6$, $b = 7.4$ and $c = 8.5$.

5 $F = 1.8C + 32$ Calculate the value of C when $F = 95$.

6 $A = \frac{1}{2}(a+b)h$ Calculate the value of b when $A = 112$, $a = 13$ and $h = 7$.

7 $A = 4\pi r^2$ Calculate correct to 3 s.f. the positive value of r when $A = 150$.

8 $v = u - gt$ Calculate the value of t when $v = 4$, $u = 40$ and $g = 10$.

9 $d = \dfrac{C}{\pi}$ Calculate correct to 3 s.f. the value of C when $d = 5.9$.

10 $A = \dfrac{\pi d^2}{4}$ Calculate correct to 3 s.f. the positive value of d when $A = 85$.

11 $y = 3x^2 - 5$ Calculate the two possible values of x when $y = 43$.

12 $s = \dfrac{(u+v)t}{2}$ Calculate the value of u when $s = 136$, $v = 25$ and $t = 8$.

13 $H = 17 - \dfrac{A}{2}$ Calculate the value of A when $H = 12\frac{1}{2}$.

14 $E = \frac{1}{2}m(v^2 - u^2)$ Calculate the positive value of u when $E = 432$, $m = 12$ and $v = 11$.

15 $y = \dfrac{10}{x-2}$ Calculate the value of x when $y = -2$.

16 $F = \dfrac{mv^2}{r}$ Calculate the positive value of v when $F = 20$, $m = 8$ and $r = 10$.

17 $V = \frac{4}{3}\pi r^3$ Calculate correct to 3 s.f. the value of r when $V = 200$.

18 $v = \sqrt{2gh}$ Calculate the value of h when $v = 8$ and $g = 10$.

19 $D = 5\sqrt{\dfrac{h}{2}}$ Calculate the value of h when $D = 8.5$.

20 $v = \omega\sqrt{a^2 - x^2}$ Calculate the positive value of x when $v = 48$, $\omega = 6$ and $a = 17$.

Exercise 5G   Mixed questions

1 For sequences with these nth terms, find
   (a) the first five terms of the sequence,
   (b) the twentieth term of the sequence.
      (i) $9n - 7$ **(ii)** $8n + 3$ **(iii)** $40 - 6n$ **(iv)** $2 - 3n$

2 Here are the first five terms of some sequences.
   Find an expression for the nth term of each of the sequences.
   (a) 3, 10, 17, 24, 31, ...   **(b)** 20, 17, 14, 11, 8, ...
   (c) 13, 21, 29, 37, 45, ...   **(d)** 5, 0, -5, -10, -15, ...

3 Here are the first four shapes in a sequence of shapes made
   from matchsticks:

Shape	Shape	Shape	Shape
number 1	number 2	number 3	number 4

   (a) Work out the number of matchsticks in shape number 5
         and in shape number 6.
   (b) Find an expression for the number of matchsticks in shape
         number n.
   (c) Find the number of matchsticks in shape number 23.
   (d) Find the shape number of the shape with 56 matchsticks.
   (e) Find the shape number of the largest shape which can be
         made with 200 matchsticks.

4 Here are four patterns made with octagonal tiles and square tiles:

 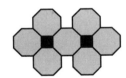 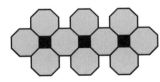 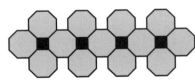

Pattern	Pattern	Pattern	Pattern
number 1	number 2	number 3	number 4

   (a) Work out the *total* number of tiles in pattern number 5
         and in pattern number 6.
   (b) Find an expression for the number of *octagonal* tiles in
         pattern number n.
   (c) Find an expression for the *total* number of tiles in pattern
         number n.
   (d) Find the number of octagonal tiles in pattern number 12.
   (e) Find the total number of tiles in pattern number 25.
   (f) Find the number of octagonal tiles in a pattern with 13
         square tiles.
   (g) Find the total number of tiles in a pattern with 58
         octagonal tiles.

5   The diagram shows a cuboid with a square base.
    The length of each side of its base is x and its height is h.
    T is the total length of the edges of the cuboid.
    (a) Find a formula for T in terms of x and h.

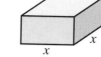

   (b) Show that $h = \dfrac{T - 8x}{4}$.

   (c) Find a formula in terms of x and T for the volume, V, of
        the cuboid.

6   $e = V + IR$
    (a) Calculate the value of e when $V = 25$, $I = 7$ and $R = 4$.
    (b) Calculate the value of R when $e = 64$, $V = 19$ and $I = 5$.

7   $y = 5 - 3x$
    (a) Calculate the value of y when $x = -4$.
    (b) Calculate the value of x when $y = -16$.

8   $L = \pi(R + r) + 2c$
    (a) Calculate correct to 3 s.f. the value of L when $R = 9.6$,
         $r = 5.3$ and $c = 8.7$.
    (b) Calculate correct to 2 s.f. the value of r when $L = 53.8$,
         $R = 8.9$ and $c = 7.6$.

9   $I = \dfrac{kP}{d^2}$
    (a) Calculate the value of I when $k = 8$, $P = 15$ and $d = 4$.
    (b) Calculate the positive value of d when $I = 3$, $k = 80$ and
         $P = 15$.

10 $r = \sqrt{\dfrac{A}{4\pi}}$
    (a) Calculate correct to 3 s.f. the positive value of r when
         $A = 70$.
    (b) Calculate correct to 3 s.f. the value of A when $r = 4.8$.

11 $V = \pi h(R^2 - r^2)$
    (a) Calculate correct to 3 s.f. the value of V when $h = 9.7$,
         $R = 8.2$ and $r = 4.5$.
    (b) Calculate correct to 2 s.f. the positive value of R when
         $V = 1400$, $h = 8.9$ and $r = 1.7$.

12 $A = \sqrt{s(s - a)(s - b)(s - c)}$ and $s = \dfrac{a + b + c}{2}$.
    Calculate the value of A when $a = 9$, $b = 12$ and $c = 15$.

Summary of key points

■ A sequence is a succession of numbers formed according
   to a rule.

■ The numbers in a sequence are called the *terms* of the
   sequence.

■ **You should recognize these common sequences:**

- even numbers   2, 4, 6, 8, 10, 12, ...
- odd numbers   1, 3, 5, 7, 9, 11, ...
- square numbers   1, 4, 9, 16, 25, 36, ...
- triangular numbers   1, 3, 6, 10, 15, 21, ...
- cube numbers   1, 8, 27, 64, 125, ...
- powers, e.g. powers of 2   2, 4, 8, 16, 32, 64, ...
- multiples, e.g. multiples of 3   3, 6, 9, 12, 15, 18, ...

■ **When you know a formula for the nth term of a sequence, you can calculate any term of the sequence by substituting a value for n in the formula. n must be a positive integer ($n = 1, 2, 3, \ldots$).**

■ **Your syllabus only includes the nth terms of sequences in which the same number is added to or subtracted from a term to obtain the next term.**

■ **A formula is a quick way of expressing a rule. It describes a relationship between two sets of numbers.**

■ **You can sometimes eliminate one of the letters from a formula by substituting for it an expression from a second formula.**

■ **You need to be able to evaluate formulae by substituting values into them. This includes negative numbers and fractions.**

■ **To find the value of a letter which is not the subject of a formula, you substitute into the formula the values given and then solve the resulting equation.**

6 Graphs, linear and quadratic

6.1 Linear graphs

■ **Expressions of the type $ax + b$ are known as *linear*.**

Teaching reference:
(*pp 143–145, section 7.1*)

Example 1

Plot the graph of $2x + 3y + 24 = 0$.

As this has no powers of x or y and no xy terms you know that it will be a straight line. Where are the intercepts with the axes?

When $x = 0$, $3y + 24 = 0$. This makes $y = -8$.
One coordinate is $(0, -8)$.

When $y = 0$, $2x + 24 = 0$. This makes $x = -12$.
Another coordinate is $(-12, 0)$.

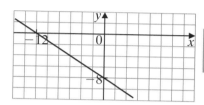

The graph has to include intercepts at $x = -12$ and $y = -8$.
It runs across the third quadrant.

As it is known to be a straight line no other point is needed, although an additional point as a check would be a good idea.

Exercise 6A   Links (7A)

For each question draw the graph of the equation. Your graph must intercept both axes.

1 $y = 2x - 11$ **2** $y + x = -7$

3 $2y = 3x + 5$ **4** $y = 2x + 25$

5 $2x + 3y + 30 = 0$ **6** $3x + 4y + 360 = 0$

7 $3y - 2x = 30$ **8** $5y = 3x - 60$

6.2 Quadratic graphs

■ **Expressions of the type $ax^2 + bx + c$, where $a \neq 0$, are known as *quadratic*.**

Teaching reference:
(*pp 323–324, section 18.1*)

Example 2

Draw the graph of the equation $y = x^2 + 3x - 18$.

One coordinate is obvious. When $x = 0$, $y = -18$. This is the intercept on the y-axis.

Where are the intercepts on the x-axis?

This will be when $x^2 + 3x - 18 = 0$

$$(x + 6)(x - 3) = 0$$

Therefore the intercepts are at $x = -6$ and $x = 3$.

The range of points needs to include -6 and 3 at least.

x	-7	-6	-5	-4	-3	-2	-1	0	1	2	3	4
x^2	49	36	25	16	9	4	1	0	1	4	9	16
$+ 3x$	-21	-18	-15	-12	-9	-6	-3	0	3	6	9	12
$- 18$	-18	-18	-18	-18	-18	-18	-18	-18	-18	-18	-18	-18
y	10	0	-8	-14	-18	-20	-20	-18	-14	-8	0	10

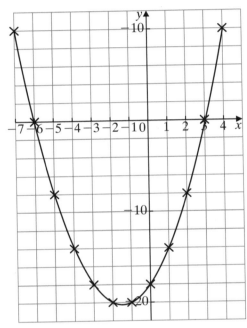

As a check, remember that these quadratic graphs are *always* symmetrical.

Exercise 6B   **Links (*18A*) 18A**

Draw graphs for each of the following equations. For 1–8, $-4 \leqslant x \leqslant 4$.

1 $y = 2x^2$

2 $y = x^2 + 2$

3 $y = x^2 + 2x - 8$

4 $y = x^2 - 3x + 4$

5 $y = 2x^2 - 5x + 3$

6 $y = 3x^2 - 7x - 6$

7 $y = 4x^2 - 12x - 7$

8 $y = 5x^2 - 2x - 72$

9 $y = (x - 15) \times (x - 20)$

10 $y = (x + 6)(x + 10)$

11 $y = x^2 + 3x - 1$

6.3 Interpreting graphical information

Example 3

The graph shows the electricity use in a small town one evening. Describe the change in demand during the evening.

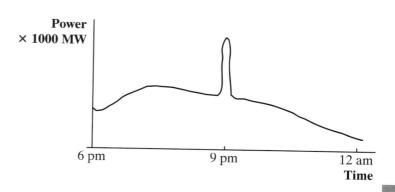

At the beginning of the evening there is a gradual increase in demand (possibly due to people coming home from work). It then tails off to a fairly constant rate with a sudden surge in demand at around 9:00 pm (typically caused at the end of a very popular TV programme). Demand declines as the evening wears on (as people go to bed).

Unless stated otherwise, the examiner is looking for the mathematical description rather than the speculation (which is in brackets).

Exercise 6C   **Links** *(18G)* **18G**

---

1   The graph shows the numbers of cars passing a traffic junction. Explain, with possible reasons, the pattern of traffic flow during the day.

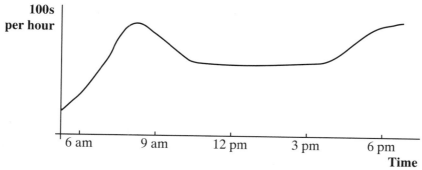

2   The graph shows the amount a hanging spring stretches as weight is added. Describe what happens.

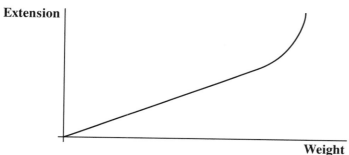

3 The graph shows house prices between 1980 and 2000.
Describe what happened to prices during these years.

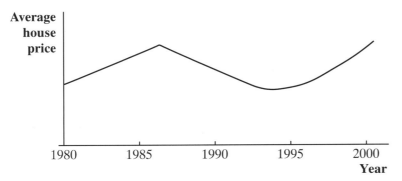

4 The distance–time graph shows the progress of a car.
Describe what happens during this part of the journey.

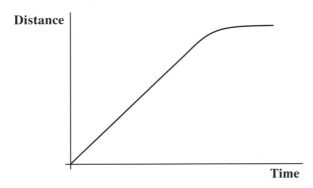

5 Sketch a graph to show the depth of
fine sand in a funnel as the sand
flows out at a constant rate.

Summary of key points

- Expressions of the type $ax + b$ are known as *linear*.
- Expressions of the type $ax^2 + bx + c$, where $a \neq 0$, are
  known as *quadratic*.

7 Pythagoras, circle properties

7.1 Pythagoras' theorem

Teaching reference:
(*pp 160–167, section 8.1*)
pp 175–183, section 18.1

■ Pythagoras' theorem states that in a right-angled triangle the square on the hypotenuse is equal to the sum of the squares on the other two sides.

$$a^2 + b^2 = c^2$$
$$\text{or} \quad c^2 = a^2 + b^2$$

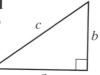

Example 1

In this right-angled triangle calculate the length of the side c:

Using Pythagoras' theorem:
$$c^2 = a^2 + b^2$$
$$c^2 = 12^2 + 9^2$$
$$= 144 + 81$$
$$= 225$$
So $\quad c = \sqrt{225} = 15\,\text{cm}$

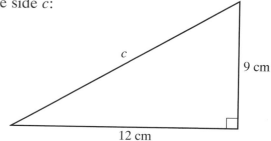

Example 2

Calculate the length AB on the coordinate grid:

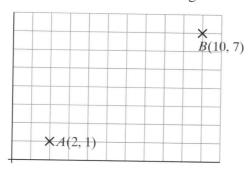

Construct a right-angled triangle ABC.

Then length $AC = 10 - 2 = 8$
length $CB = 7 - 1 = 6$

So using Pythagoras:
$$AB^2 = 8^2 + 6^2$$
$$= 64 + 36$$
$$= 100$$
Then $\quad AB = \sqrt{100} = 10$

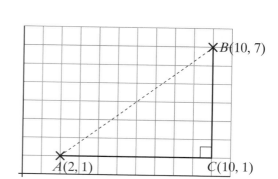

■ Given the coordinates $A(x_1, y_1)$ and $B(x_2, y_2)$ the length $AB = \sqrt{(x_2 - x_1)^2 + (y_2 - y_1)^2}$

■ To calculate one of the shorter sides in a right-angled triangle use $a^2 = c^2 - b^2$ or $b^2 = c^2 - a^2$.

Example 3

Calculate the length of d correct to 3 significant figures:

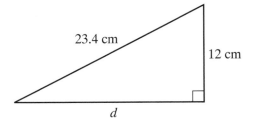

$$d^2 = 23.4^2 - 12^2$$
$$= 547.56 - 144$$
$$= 403.56$$
so $d = \sqrt{403.56}$
$$= 20.1 \text{ cm to 3 s.f.}$$

Example 4

Triangle PQR is isosceles. (Remember that a perpendicular from any vertex to an opposite side bisects that side). Calculate the height of the triangle.

Construct a perpendicular to PQ at its mid-point M. Then PRM is a right-angled triangle with $PM = 4$ cm. To calculate height RM use Pythagoras:

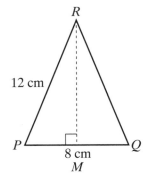

$$RM^2 = 12^2 - 4^2$$
$$RM^2 = 144 - 16$$
$$= 128$$
so $RM = \text{height} = \sqrt{128}$
$$= 11.3 \text{ to 3 s.f.}$$

Exercise 7A   **Links (8A, 8B, 8C, 8D) 8A, 8B, 8C, 8D**

1   Calculate the lengths marked with letters in these triangles:

(a)

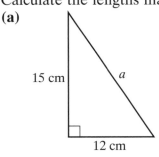

15 cm, a, 12 cm

(b)

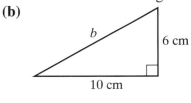

b, 6 cm, 10 cm

(c)

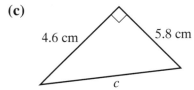

4.6 cm, 5.8 cm, c

(d)

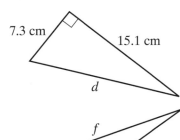

7.3 cm, 15.1 cm, d

(e)

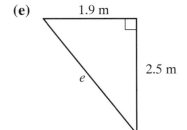

1.9 m, 2.5 m, e

(f)

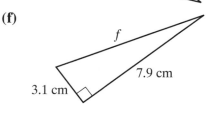

f, 7.9 cm, 3.1 cm

2 Calculate the length AB for the following coordinates of the points A and B:

(a) $A(0,0)$, $B(3,4)$ (b) $A(0,0)$, $B(9,12)$
(c) $A(0,0)$, $B(4,7)$ (d) $A(2,3)$, $B(5,7)$
(e) $A(1,9)$, $B(4,11)$ (f) $A(3,12)$, $B(7,4)$.

3 Calculate the lengths marked with letters in these triangles:

(a)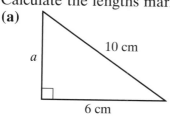

(b)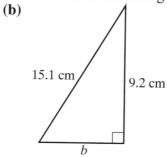

(c)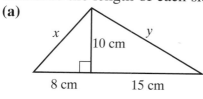

(d)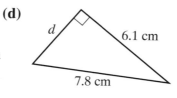

4 A rectangle measures 12 cm by 28 cm. Calculate the length of a diagonal.

5 An isosceles triangle PQR has two equal sides 12 cm in length and a base 10 cm in length.
Calculate the height of the triangle.

6 Calculate the length of each side marked with a letter:

(a)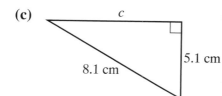

(b)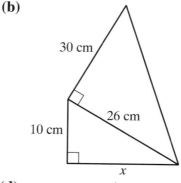

(c)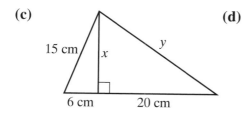

(d)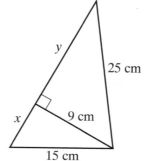

7.2 Properties of circles

■ **A circle is the shape enclosed by a curve which is everywhere the same distance from the centre.**

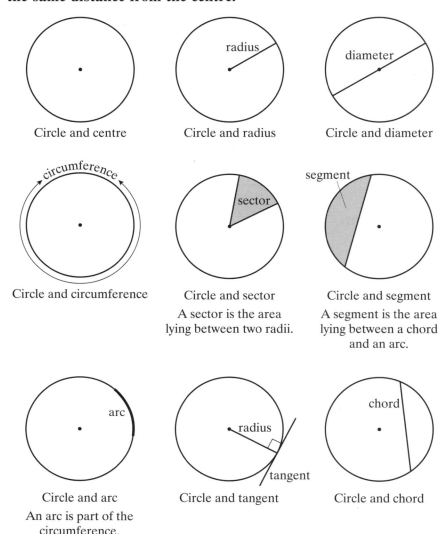

Circle and centre   Circle and radius   Circle and diameter

Circle and circumference   Circle and sector   Circle and segment
                            A sector is the area   A segment is the area
                            lying between two radii.   lying between a chord
                                                       and an arc.

Circle and arc   Circle and tangent   Circle and chord
An arc is part of the
circumference.

■ **The circumference of a circle is the distance measured around the curve which makes the circle.**
■ **A chord is a straight line drawn across a circle.**
■ **A tangent to a circle touches the circle at one point only. The radius is at 90° to the tangent.**

Exercise 7B	Links (*3F*)

1   Draw a diagram to show radius, diameter and circumference.
2   Draw a diagram to show arc, circumference and tangent.
3   Draw a diagram to show chord, sector and segment.

7.3 Properties of circles and tangents

Theorem:

Teaching reference:
(*pp 502–505, section 28.1*)
pp 524–527, section 26.1

- **The lengths of the two tangents from a point are equal.**

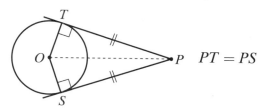 $PT = PS$

This follows by symmetry: OP is a mirror line.

Example 5

In the diagram, calculate TO.

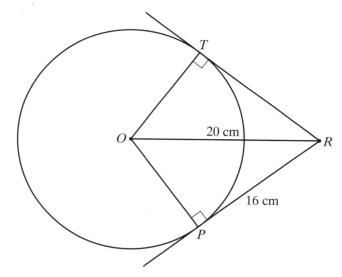

Using the theorem above:

$TR = PR$, so $TR = 16$ cm

$$OT^2 = OR^2 - TR^2$$
$$OT^2 = 20^2 - 16^2$$
$$OT^2 = 400 - 256$$
$$OT^2 = 144$$
$$OT = \sqrt{144} = 12 \text{ cm}$$

Example 6

Calculate angle TOP:

$\angle OPT = 28°$ (triangles OTP and OSP are congruent, so angles OPT and OPS are equal)
$\angle TOP = 180° - 90° - 28°$
$\qquad = 62°$

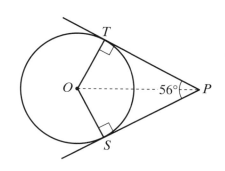

1 PQ and PR are tangents to the circle centre O.

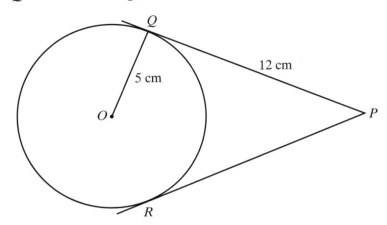

The radius of the circle is 5 cm and the length of the tangent is 12 cm.
Calculate PO.

2   In the diagram PT and PS are tangents to the circle.
Calculate SO.

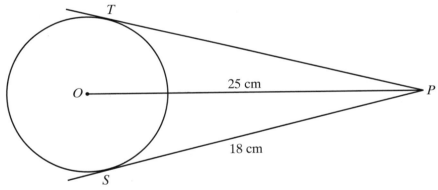

3 PR and PQ are tangents to the circle.
Calculate angle POR.

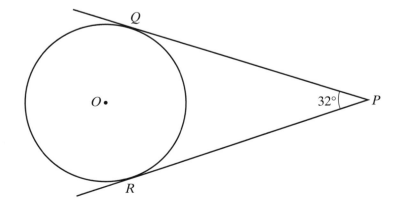

4 *PR* and *PQ* are tangents to the circle.
Calculate angle *POQ*.

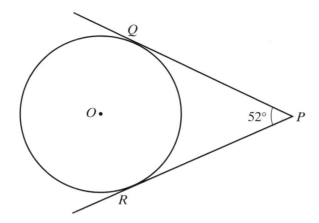

Where an answer is not exact quote it to 3 s.f.

1 Calculate the lengths of the sides marked with a letter:

(a)

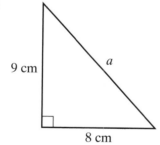

(b)

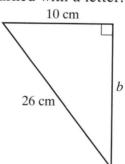

2 Calculate the distances between the points
(a) $(5, 2)$ and $(11, 6)$
(b) $(-2, -5)$ and $(3, 0)$.

3 Calculate the length *AB* in this shape:

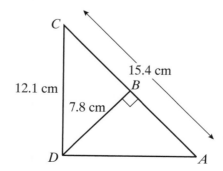

4 An isosceles triangle *ABC* has two equal sides of length 20 cm and a height of 14 cm.
Calculate the length of the base of the triangle.

5 *PS* and *PR* are tangents to the circle (radius 8 cm). *PO* is 16 cm.
Calculate the length of *PS* and angle *POR*.

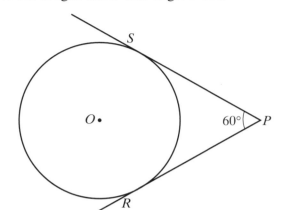

6 Madhavi places her ladder 2 m away from a vertical wall to reach a height of 7 m.
Calculate the length of the ladder.

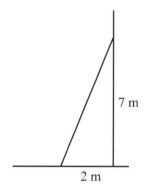

7 Pete and Sue sail due North from a buoy for 10 km. They then sail due East for 14 km.
How far is the boat from the buoy?

8 A square has diagonals of length 15 cm. Calculate the length of each side.

Summary of key points

■ **Pythagoras' theorem states that in a right-angled triangle the square on the hypotenuse is equal to the sum of the squares on the other two sides.**

$$a^2 + b^2 = c^2$$
$$\text{or} \quad c^2 = a^2 + b^2$$

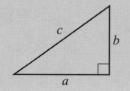

- Given the coordinates $A(x_1, y_1)$ and $B(x_2, y_2)$ the length
$AB = \sqrt{(x_2 - x_1)^2 + (y_2 - y_1)^2}$

- To calculate one of the shorter sides in a right-angled triangle use $a^2 = c^2 - b^2$ or $b^2 = c^2 - a^2$.

- A circle is the shape enclosed by a curve which is everywhere the same distance from the centre.

- The circumference of a circle is the distance measured around the curve which makes the circle.

- A chord is a straight line drawn across a circle.

- A tangent to a circle touches the circle at one point only. The radius is at 90° to the tangent.

- The lengths of the two tangents from a point are equal.

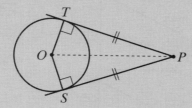

8 Trigonometry

8.1 The three trigonometric functions

Teaching reference:
(*pp 226–234, sections 13.1, 13.2, 13.3*)
pp 268–274, sections 13.1, 13.2

■ The three basic trigonometric functions are $\sin x$, $\cos x$ and $\tan x$.

Example 1
Find the value of $\cos 38°$ to 3 s.f.
Using a calculator: $\cos 38° = 0.788$.

Example 2
Find the value of x for $\sin x = 0.89$.
Using a calculator $x = 63°$.

You will need to use inv, 2nd function or arcsin to find the value of x.

■ $\sin x = \dfrac{\text{opp}}{\text{hyp}}$

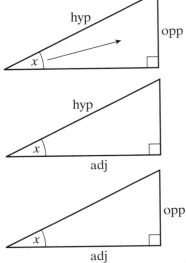

opp = opposite
hyp = hypotenuse
adj = adjacent

■ $\cos x = \dfrac{\text{adj}}{\text{hyp}}$

These ratios can only be used in right-angled triangles.

■ $\tan x = \dfrac{\text{opp}}{\text{adj}}$

Example 3
Calculate the size of the angle at A:

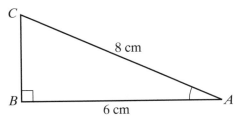

AC is the hypotenuse and AB is the adjacent. So use the cosine ratio:

$$\cos A = \frac{\text{adj}}{\text{hyp}}$$

so $\cos A = \dfrac{6}{8}$

$\cos A = 0.75$

$A = 41.4°$ to 3 s.f.

Example 4

Calculate the size of the angle at D:

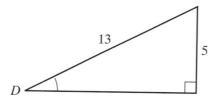

We know the hypotenuse and the opposite so use the sine ratio:

$$\sin D = \frac{\text{opp}}{\text{hyp}}$$
$$= \frac{5}{13}$$
$$= 0.3846$$
$$D = 22.6° \text{ to 3 s.f.}$$

Example 5

Calculate angle y.

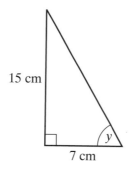

We know the opposite and the adjacent so use the tangent ratio:

$$\tan y = \frac{\text{opp}}{\text{adj}}$$
$$\tan y = \frac{15}{7} = 2.143$$
$$y = 65.0 \text{ to 3 s.f.}$$

Exercise 8A　　**Links (*13A, 13B, 13C, 13D*) 13A, 13B, 13C**

1　Use your calculator to find these ratios:

(a)　$\cos 37°$　　　(b)　$\tan 45°$　　　(c)　$\cos 60°$
(d)　$\sin 90°$　　　(e)　$\cos 78°$　　　(f)　$\sin 12°$
(g)　$\tan 31°$　　　(h)　$\sin 48°$　　　(i)　$\cos 43°$
(j)　$\sin 71°$　　　(k)　$\tan 69°$　　　(l)　$\cos 21°$

2   Use your calculator to find each angle x when
   (a) $\sin x = 0.707$ (b) $\tan x = 3.07$
   (c) $\cos x = 0.559$ (d) $\tan x = 0.445$
   (e) $\sin x = 0.123$ (f) $\cos x = 0.978$

3   In this question all lengths are in centimetres.
   Calculate each of the angles marked with a letter.

(a)
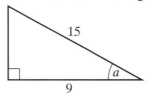

(b)
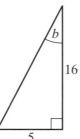

(c)
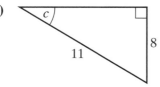

(d)
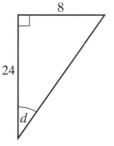

(e)
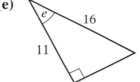

(f)
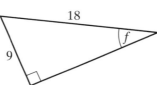

(g)

(h)
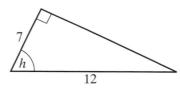

8.2 Using the three trigonometric functions to find missing sides

Example 6

Calculate the length of the side marked x:

We are given one angle (38°) and the hypotenuse, 12 cm.
We want to calculate the adjacent.

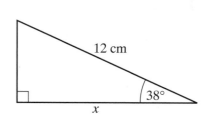

So we use the cosine ratio $\cos x = \dfrac{\text{adj}}{\text{hyp}}$:

$$\cos 38° = \frac{x}{12}$$

$$\therefore \qquad x = 12 \times \cos 38°$$

$$x = 9.46 \text{ cm to 3 s.f.}$$

Example 7

Calculate the length of the side marked w:

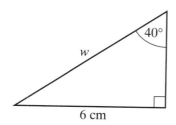

For angle given, $40°$, w is the hypotenuse and the 6 cm side is the opposite.

So use $\qquad \sin x = \dfrac{\text{opp}}{\text{hyp}}$

$$\sin 40° = \frac{6}{w}$$

so $\qquad w = \dfrac{6}{\sin 40°}$

$$w = 9.33 \text{ cm to 3 s.f.}$$

Exercise 8B   Links (*13E*) 13E

In this exercise all lengths are in centimetres.
Calculate the length marked with a letter.

(a)

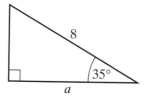

(b)

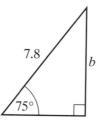

(c)

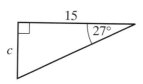

(d)

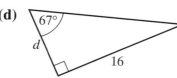

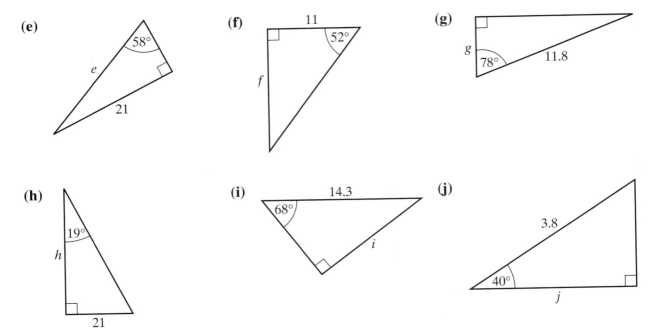

(e) 58° e 21

(f) 11 52° f

(g) g 78° 11.8

(h) 19° h 21

(i) 14.3 68° i

(j) 3.8 40° j

8.3 The three trigonometric functions applied to bearing problems

Example 8

A yacht sails on a bearing of 135° for 8 km. It changes to a bearing of 030° and sails 20 km. How far East of its original position is it?

First draw a diagram:

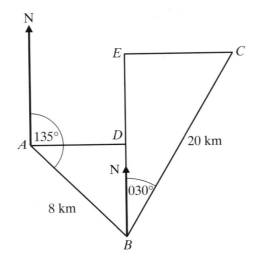

> Remember: bearings are measured from North in a clockwise direction. They have three figures.

The distance East is $AD + EC$.

To find *AD*:

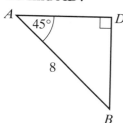

We have hypotenuse = 8, angle = 45°.
We need to calculate the adjacent.
So use cosine ratio:

$$\cos 45° = \frac{AD}{8}$$
$$AD = 8 \times \cos 45°$$
$$AD = 5.66 \text{ to 3 s.f.}$$

To find *EC*:

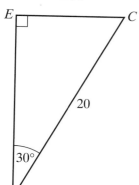

We have hypotenuse = 20, angle = 30°.
We need opposite so use sine ratio:

$$\sin 30° = \frac{EC}{20}$$
$$EC = 20 \times \sin 30°$$
$$EC = 10$$

So total distance east = 5.66 + 10
= 15.7 km to 3 s.f.

Exercise 8C ∘ Mixed questions Links (*13F*) 13F

1 Calculate the size of the sides marked with letters:

(a)

15 cm

a

32°

(b)

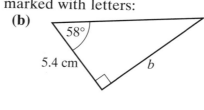

58°

5.4 cm

b

2 A ship sails on a bearing of 040° for 12 km, followed by a bearing of 128° for 8 km. Calculate the distance the ship is East of its starting point.

3 Bob the builder places his 7-metre ladder to make an angle of 68° with the horizontal ground, against a vertical wall.
(a) How far is the foot of the ladder from the wall?
(b) How far up the wall is the top of the ladder?

4 The angle of elevation of the top of a church spire from a point 1 metre above horizontal ground, at a distance of 18 m from the spire, is 51°. Calculate the height of the spire.

5 A boat is 25 km due South of a harbour, H.
A marker buoy, B, is 18 km due East of H.
(a) How far is the boat from the marker buoy?
(b) Calculate the bearing of the boat from B.

6 The diagram represents a roof truss:

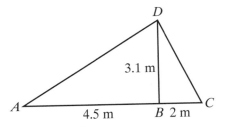

(a) Calculate the length DC.
(b) Calculate the size of angle DAB.

7 A buoy, B, is 50 km from harbour H on a bearing of 050°.
A lighthouse, L, is 120 km from the buoy, B, on a bearing of
142°.
A ship sails from harbour H to lighthouse L.
Calculate the shortest distance between the ship and the buoy
during its journey.

Summary of key points

■ The three basic trigonometric functions are $\sin x$, $\cos x$ and
$\tan x$.

■ $\sin x = \dfrac{\text{opp}}{\text{hyp}}$

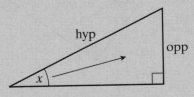

■ $\cos x = \dfrac{\text{adj}}{\text{hyp}}$

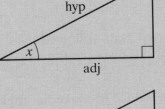

■ $\tan x = \dfrac{\text{opp}}{\text{adj}}$

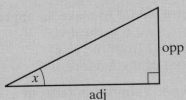

9 Transformations

9.1 Translation

- A translation moves every point on a shape the same distance and direction. A translation is described by a vector $\begin{pmatrix} x \\ y \end{pmatrix}$.

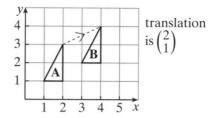

translation is $\begin{pmatrix} 2 \\ 1 \end{pmatrix}$

Example 1

Write down the vector describing the translation **A** to **B**.

The translation is $\begin{pmatrix} 4 \\ -5 \end{pmatrix}$.

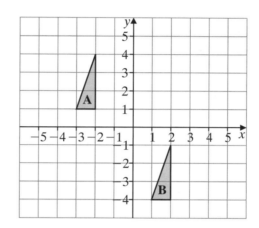

Exercise 9A	Links (6C)

1   Write the vector describing each of the translations that map **A** onto these other shapes:

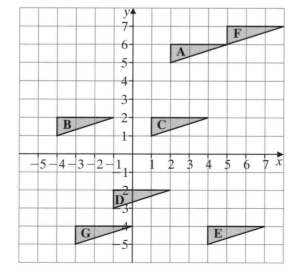

2 Use graph paper or squared paper.
Draw a set of axes and label each one from -7 to $+7$.
Draw a quadrilateral **Q** with points $A(-1, 2)$, $B(-3, 3)$, $C(1, 4)$ and $D(1, 2)$.
Translate **Q** using the following vectors:

(a) $\begin{pmatrix} 2 \\ 1 \end{pmatrix}$ (b) $\begin{pmatrix} -1 \\ 1 \end{pmatrix}$ (c) $\begin{pmatrix} -2 \\ -3 \end{pmatrix}$ (d) $\begin{pmatrix} 4 \\ -1 \end{pmatrix}$

(e) $\begin{pmatrix} 1 \\ -1 \end{pmatrix}$ (f) $\begin{pmatrix} 3 \\ 0 \end{pmatrix}$ (g) $\begin{pmatrix} -1 \\ -2 \end{pmatrix}$ (h) $\begin{pmatrix} -2 \\ 3 \end{pmatrix}$

9.2 Reflection

■ **A reflection produces a mirror image in a line of symmetry.**

■ **A repeated reflection in the same line of symmetry returns the image to the original shape.**

■ **A reflection of a shape can be described by giving the equation of the line of symmetry.**

Example 2

On the diagram draw a reflection of the shape in
(a) $y = x$ and (b) $y = -x$.
Call them **P** and **Q**.

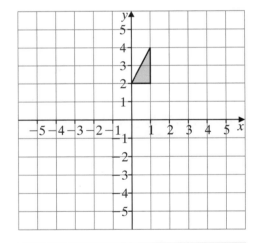

Take each vertex on the object and locate its image (use a line perpendicular to the line of symmetry). Join the points to produce the image.

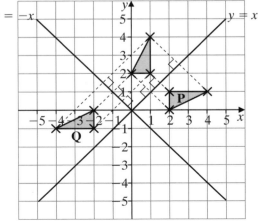

Exercise 9B   **Links** (*6D*) **6D**

1   Copy the diagram.
For each shape reflect it in the mirror line M.

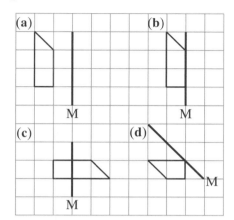

2   Shape **A** has been reflected 4 times.
Describe fully the reflection that takes **A** to
   (a) P   **(b) Q**   **(c) R**   **(d) S**

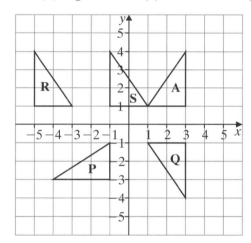

9.3 Rotation

■   **A rotation is described by giving**

- **a centre of rotation**
- **an amount of turn**
- **a direction of turn.**

(A clockwise direction may be indicated by a negative sign, and an anticlockwise direction by a positive sign.)

Triangle A is turned 120° clockwise about a **centre of rotation.**

■   **A rotation is defined by its centre and the angle and direction of turn.**

Example 3

Describe the transformation
which takes **A** to **B**.

Rotation centre $(1, 1)$
through $90°$.

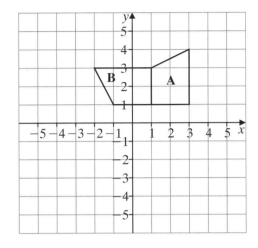

Example 4

Rotate shape **A** about the origin through $-90°$.

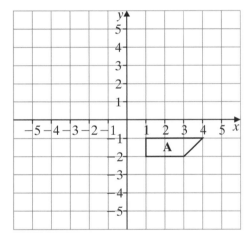

Each vertex of the quadrilateral must be rotated $90°$ clockwise:

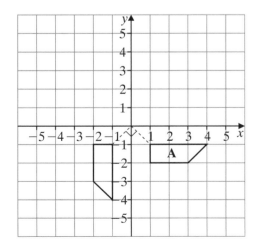

Exercise 9C   **Links** (*6E*) **6E**

1   Copy this diagram. Transform shape **R** by
       the following rotations:
       (a) centre $(0,0)$ $-270°$
       (b) centre $(2,1)$ $+90°$
       (c) centre $(-1,2)$ $+180°$
       (d) centre $(0,0)$ $-90°$.

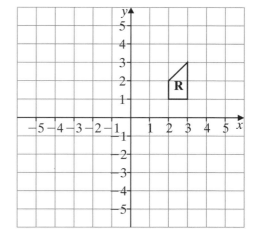

2   Shape **T** has been rotated 4 times. Describe
       fully the rotation that takes **T** to position
       (a) A   **(b) B**   **(c) C**   **(d) D**

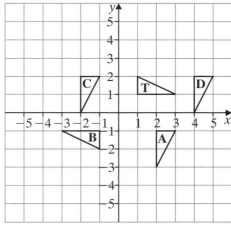

3   Copy and complete this table:

Rotation	Transforms
centre $(0,0)$, $90°$	point $(1,2)$ to ____
centre $(0,0)$, $-180°$	point $(3,5)$ to ____
centre $(-1,2)$, $-90°$	point $(2,3)$ to ____
centre $(2,4)$, $270°$	point $(2,-1)$ to ____
centre $(0,0$ $-270°$	point $(-1,4)$ to ____

9.4 Enlargement

■ **An enlargement made with a scale factor smaller than 1 gives
   a reduced image.**

■ **An enlargement made with a negative scale factor indicates
   that the measuring from the centre of enlargement must be in
   the opposite direction.**

■ **An enlargement is defined by its centre and scale factor.**

Example 5

Enlarge trapezium *ABCD* with scale factor $1\frac{1}{2}$ using the origin as the centre of enlargement.

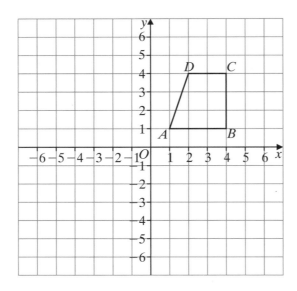

An enlargement scale factor $1\frac{1}{2}$ enlarges each side of the quadrilateral by $1\frac{1}{2}$.
So

$$OA \times 1\tfrac{1}{2} = OA'$$
$$OB \times 1\tfrac{1}{2} = OB'$$
$$OC \times 1\tfrac{1}{2} = OC'$$
$$OD \times 1\tfrac{1}{2} = OD'$$

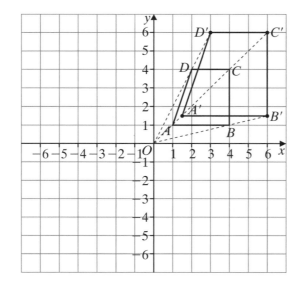

Notice each coordinate is multiplied by $1\frac{1}{2}$.

So

$$A\,(1,1) \rightarrow A'\,(1\tfrac{1}{2}, 1\tfrac{1}{2})$$
$$B\,(4,1) \rightarrow B'\,(6, 1\tfrac{1}{2})$$
$$C\,(4,4) \rightarrow C'\,(6,6)$$
$$D\,(2,4) \rightarrow D'\,(3,6)$$

Example 6

Enlarge triangle ABC by scale factor -1 and centre $(0,0)$.

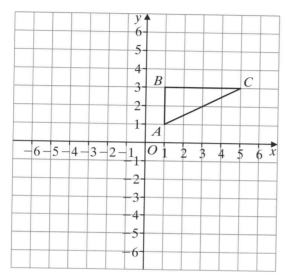

A negative scale factor means measuring from the centre of the enlargement in the opposite direction.

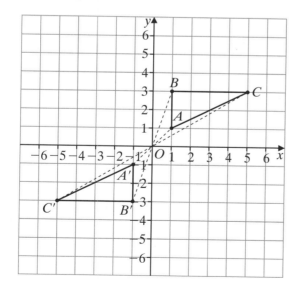

So

$$OA \times -1 = OA'$$
$$OB \times -1 = OB'$$
$$OC \times -1 = OC'$$

Exercise 9D   Links (*6F*) 6F

1   Copy this shape.
    Draw the enlargement
    (a) centre $(0, 0)$,
         scale factor of enlargement 2
    (b) centre $(1, 2)$,
         scale factor of enlargement 2.

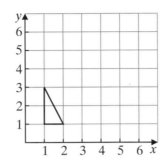

2   Copy this shape.

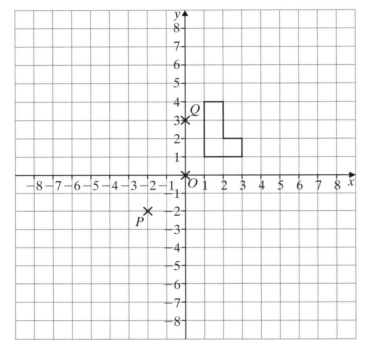

    Enlarge it by the following:
    (a) scale factor 2, centre O
    (b) scale factor -1, centre P
    (c) scale factor $+0.5$, centre O
    (d) scale factor $1\frac{1}{2}$, centre Q
    (e) scale factor -1.5, centre O.

3   Look at the following diagrams. Describe the enlargement that
    moves
    (a) **A → B**
    (b) **A → C**
    (c) **A → D**
    (d) **A → E**
    (e) **A → F**

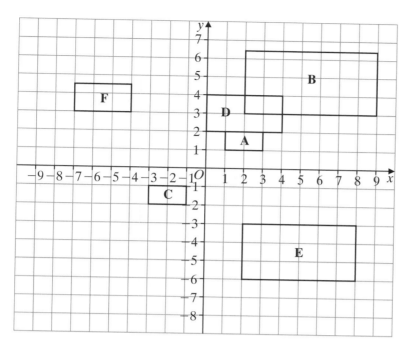

4   Copy this diagram.

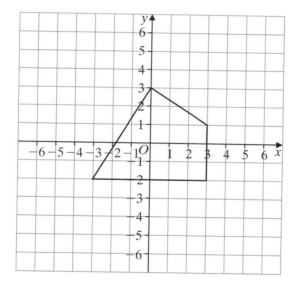

Enlarge the shape by scale factor -2 centre $(0,0)$.

Summary of key points

■   A translation moves every point on a shape the same
     distance and direction. A translation is described by a

     vector $\begin{pmatrix} x \\ y \end{pmatrix}$.

- A reflection produces a mirror image in a line of symmetry.

- A repeated reflection in the same line of symmetry returns the image to the original shape.

- A reflection of a shape can be described by giving the equation of the line of symmetry.

- A rotation is described by giving
  - a centre of rotation
  - an amount of turn
  - a direction of turn.

  (A clockwise direction may be indicated by a negative sign, and an anticlockwise direction by a positive sign.)

- A rotation is defined by its centre and the angle and direction of turn.

- An enlargement made with a scale factor smaller than 1 gives a reduced image.

- An enlargement made with a negative scale factor indicates that the measuring from the centre of enlargement must be in the opposite direction.

- An enlargement is defined by its centre and scale factor.

10 Mensuration

10.1 Area of plane shapes

- The area of a triangle is $\frac{1}{2}$ base × height or $\frac{1}{2}bh$.
- The area of a parallelogram is base × perpendicular height.
- The area of a trapezium is $\frac{1}{2}h(a+b)$ where a and b are the lengths of the parallel sides and h is the distance between the parallel sides.
- The area of a circle is πr^2 where r is the radius.

Example 1

Find the area of triangle ABC.
Any side of the triangle can be the base.
Choose AC as the base.
Then BD becomes the height.

$$\text{Area} = \tfrac{1}{2} \times 5 \times 8 = 20\,\text{cm}^2$$

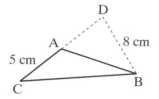

Example 2

Find the length of the side marked x.

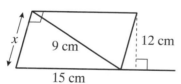

The area of the parallelogram is $15 \times 12 = 180\,\text{cm}^2$
The area is also $x \times 9$ (if x is the base)

$$x \times 9 = 180$$
$$x = 20\,\text{cm}$$

Exercise 10A   Links (*16D, 16E, 16F*) 16B, C, D, E, F

1   $ABCD$ is a rectangle with area $296\,\text{cm}^2$. The length AB is $80\,\text{mm}$. Work out the height BC.

2   Work out the area of the parallelograms shown:

(a)
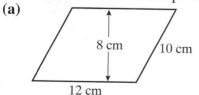

(b)
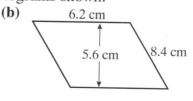

(c)
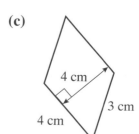

3 In each diagram, work out the value of x:

(a)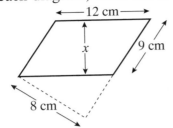

(b)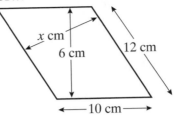

(c)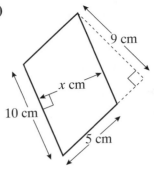

4 Work out the area of the triangles shown:

(a)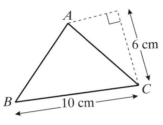

(b)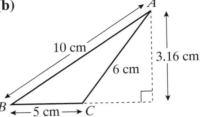

(c)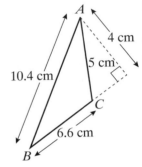

(d)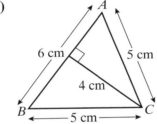

(e)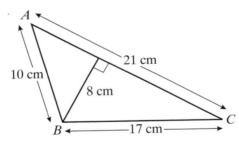

5 Find the area of each trapezium shown:

(a)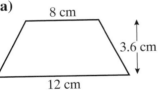

(b)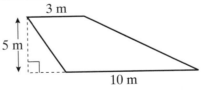

(c)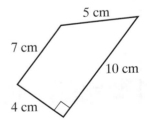

6 The ratio of the base of this trapezium to its height is $5:2$.
Work out an expression for the area of the trapezium.

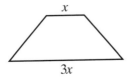

7 (a) The circumference of a circle is 84π cm. Find its area.
(b) The area of a circle is 72π. Find its circumference.

Example 3

Work out the area of the shape shown:

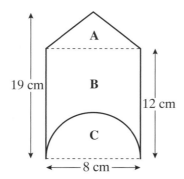

The area can be found from the area of triangle **A**, rectangle **B** and semicircle **C**. It is $\mathbf{A} + \mathbf{B} + \mathbf{C}$.

Area $\mathbf{A} = \frac{1}{2} \times 8 \times (19 - 12) = 4 \times 7 = 28\,\text{cm}^2$
Area $\mathbf{B} = 8 \times 12 = 96\,\text{cm}^2$
Area $\mathbf{C} = \frac{1}{2}\pi \times 4^2 = 8\pi = 25.13\,\text{cm}^2$
Area of the shape $= 28 + 96 - 25.13 = 98.87\,\text{cm}^2$

Exercise 10B

1 In each part work out the area:

(a)

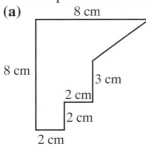

(b)

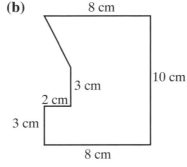

(c)

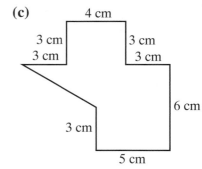

(d)

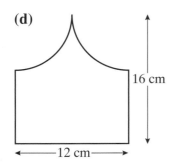

(e)

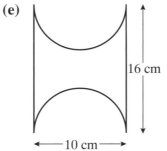

(f)

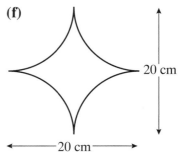

10.2 Surface area and volume of cuboids

■ **Cuboid: total length around the edges** $= 4(a + b + c)$
   surface area $= 2(ab + bc + ac)$
   volume $= abc$

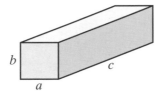

Example 4

Find the total surface area of this cuboid.
The end face measures $8\,\text{cm} \times 5\,\text{cm}$ and the volume is $480\,\text{cm}^3$.

$v = 1bh$
$480 = 5 \times 8 \times \text{length}$
$\text{length} = 12\,\text{cm}$

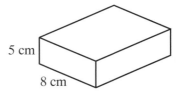

Front face area $= 8 \times 5 = 40\,\text{cm}^2$
Side face area $= 5 \times 12 = 60\,\text{cm}^2$
Top face area $= 8 \times 12 = 96\,\text{cm}^2$

As there are two of each, the total surface area $= 2(40 + 60 + 96)$
$\qquad\qquad\qquad\qquad\qquad\qquad\qquad\qquad\quad = 392\,\text{cm}^2$

Exercise 10C   Links (*16G*) 16G

1   The surface area of a cube is $96\,\text{cm}^2$.
    What is the length of an edge?

2   Work out the surface area of this cuboid.

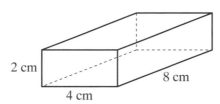

3   The sum of the three different edges of a cuboid is $15\,\text{cm}$.
    Complete this table of volumes and surface areas. Four have
    been done for you.

Size	1, 1, 13	1, 2, 12	2, 2, 11	1, 3, 11				
Volume	13	24	44	33				
Area	54	76	96	94				

Which gives the maximum volume?
Which gives the maximum surface area?

4 Copy and complete the table of values for these cuboids. All the measurements are in cm.

Height	Length	Width	Volume
5	3	2	
7	8	5	
4	8		96
	7	3	105
10		3	105

10.3 Surface area and volume of prisms

■ **The volume of a prism is base area × vertical height.**

Teaching reference:
(*pp 298–299, section 16.3*)
pp 341–342, section 16.3

Example 5

Find the volume and surface area of the triangular prism shown.

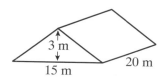

Volume = cross section area × height

$$= \tfrac{1}{2} \times 15 \times 3 \times 20 = 450 \, \text{m}^3$$

Area of triangular ends $= 2(\tfrac{1}{2} \times 15 \times 3) = 45 \, \text{m}^2$
For the sloping faces use Pythagoras to find the length.

$$\text{slanting edge} = \sqrt{7\tfrac{1}{2}^2 + 3^2} = 8.08 \, \text{m}$$

Area of rectangular faces $= 20 \times (8.08 + 8.08 + 15)$

$$= 623.2 \, \text{m}^2$$

Total surface area $= 668.2 \, \text{m}^2$

Exercise 10D   Links (*16G*) 16H

1 *ABCDEF* is a triangular-based prism.
Angle *ABC* = 90°.
AB = 5 cm, *BC* = 12 cm, *CF* = 3 cm, *AC* = 13 cm.
Work out the surface area and volume.

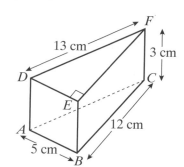

2 *ABCDEF* is a triangular-based prism.
Angle *FDE* = 90°.
DF = 8 cm, *DE* = 15 cm, *EF* = 17 cm.
Volume = 300 cm³.

Work out *BE* and the total surface area.

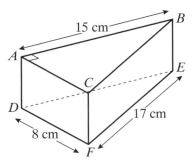

3 Calculate the volume and total surface area of the two prisms shown:

(a)

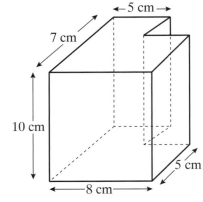

(b)

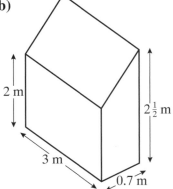

4 Work out the volume of the tunnel:

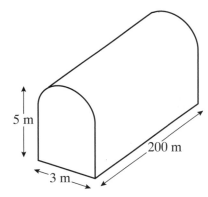

5 Work out the surface area and volume of this storage shed.
The surface area should not include the base.

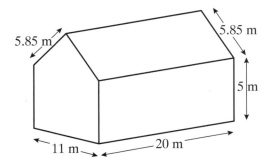

10.4 Surface area and volume of cylinders

■ For a cylinder of height h with a circular base of radius r:
surface area $= 2\pi rh + 2\pi r^2$
volume $= \pi r^2 h$

Example 6

Find the total surface area of a cylinder which has diameter 8 mm and height 32 cm.

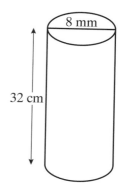

First, make sure the units are consistent so for 8 mm use 0.8 cm

Radius $= 0.4$ cm
Volume $= \pi \times (0.4)^2 \times 32 = 51.2\pi$ cm^3 (answer in terms of π)
$= 160.8$ cm^3

Surface area is made up from two circular ends wrapped round by a rectangle.
$$= 2\pi r^2 + 2\pi rh$$
$$= 2\pi \times (0.4)^2 + 2\pi \times 0.4 \times 32$$
$$= 0.32\pi + 25.6\pi = 25.9\pi \text{ cm}^2 \text{ in terms of } \pi$$
$$= 81.4 \text{ cm}^2$$

Exercise 10E   Links (*19E*) 19E

Work in centimetres throughout.

1   Work out the radii of these cylinders:
    (a) height 20 cm, volume 150 cm^3
    (b) height 15 cm, volume 200 cm^3
    (c) height 8 cm, volume 170 cm^3
    (d) height 15 mm, volume 10 cm^3
    (e) height 2 m, volume 2300 cm^3.

2   Work out the volume of these cylinders (give your answers in terms of π):
    (a) radius 5 cm, height 12 cm
    (b) radius 8 cm, height 8 cm
    (c) radius 3 cm, height 20 cm
    (d) diameter 80 mm, height 2 m
    (e) diameter 0.46 m, height 1.2 mm.

3   Work out the surface area and volume of these cylinders (give your answers to three significant figures):
    (a) radius 4 cm, height 15 cm
    (b) radius 6 cm, height 28 cm
    (c) radius 5 cm, height 2 m
    (d) radius 15 mm, height 9 cm
    (e) diameter 50 mm, height 300 cm
    (f) diameter 6 m, height 8 mm.

10.5 Using suitable units

Any unit of length could be used to measure the distance between two telegraph poles:

$\qquad$ 0.06 km $\quad$ 60 m $\quad$ 6000 cm $\quad$ 60 000 mm

All these represent the same distance, but in this case 60 m is the most sensible to use.

When working out areas and volumes the dimensions may be given in different units. Rationalise the units so that your answer comes out in an appropriate form.

Example 7

Wood weighs 700 kg per cubic metre.
Find the weight of a plank of wood measuring
2 m × 15 cm × 12 mm.

Because the weight is given per cubic metre it is best to work in metres.

$\qquad$ 15 cm = 0.15 m
$\qquad$ 12 mm = 0.012 m

Volume = 2 × 0.15 × 0.012 = 0.0036 m³
Weight = 0.0036 × 700 kg = 2.52 kg

Exercise 10F

1 $\quad$ A concrete path is to be built. It measures 20 metres long by 60 centimetres wide by 50 millimetres deep. What volume of concrete is required?

2 $\quad$ Paper weighs 80 grams per square metre. Work out the weight of a sheet of A4 paper. A4 measures 297 mm × 210 mm.

3 $\quad$ The radius of a wheel is 30 cm. How many revolutions does it make on a journey of 5 km?

4 $\quad$ A telephone wire weighs 12.5 g per cubic centimetre. The radius of the wire is 1.2 mm. How much would 1 km of wire weigh?

5 $\quad$ How many litres of water are contained in a hosepipe with diameter 20 mm and length 30 metres?

6 $\quad$ Gold leaf comes in booklets of 10 sheets which measure 50 mm by 30 mm. How many booklets are required to cover 2 m²?

10.6 Metric and Imperial equivalents

■ **You are expected to know these equivalents:**
$1 \, kg = 2.2 \, pounds \, (lb)$
$8 \, kilometres = 5 \, miles$
$1 \, litre = 1.75 \, pints$
$30 \, cm = 1 \, foot$
$2.54 \, cm = 1 \, inch$
$4.5 \, litres = 1 \, gallon$

Example 8

There are 640 acres in a square mile.
There are 100 hectares in a square kilometre.
How many acres are there in 1 hectare?

$5 \, miles = 8 \, kilometres$
This means 25 square miles = 64 square kilometres

$25 \times 640 \, acres = 64 \times 100 \, hectares$
$2.5 \, acres = 1 \, hectare$

Exercise 10G

1   A fish tank measures 3 feet × 2 feet × 1 foot. How many litres does it take to fill it?

2   A petrol tank measures $35 \, cm \times 24 \, cm \times 60 \, cm$. How many gallons will it hold?

3   Change £4.95 per pound (lb) to pence per kilogram.

4   Change 5 miles per gallon to kilometres per litre.

5   Change 3.7 kg per cubic metre to pounds (lb) per cubic foot.

6   A gallon of fertiliser covers 200 square feet. How many square metres are covered by 1 litre?

Example 9

A cow needs 0.018 hectares to feed in.
A field measures 61.3 metres by 42.3 metres.
How many cows can it support?

Area of field $= 61.3 \times 42.3 \, m^2$
1 hectare is $100 \times 100 \, m^2$

$$\text{Number of animals} = \frac{61.3 \times 42.3}{100 \times 100 \times 0.018}$$

$$= \frac{61.3 \times 42.3}{180}$$

$$\simeq \frac{60 \times 40}{200} = 12$$

There is enough space for about 12 cows.

Exercise 10H

Estimates are required in these questions.

1   1 kg of seed is enough to sow about 30 m². How much seed is required to sow 25 hectares?

2   The recommended concentration to mix a fertiliser is 17.6 g per litre. How much is needed to mix 50 gallons of fertiliser?

3   A wall is 15 m long and 2 m high. It is built to a thickness of 2 bricks. The face of each brick measures 21 cm by 6 cm. How many bricks are needed?

4   A high-pressure hose, radius 6 cm, delivers water at the rate of 50 gallons per second. At what speed is the water leaving the hose? (Hint: how long would the hose need to be to contain 50 gallons?)

5   The grain yield at a farm is known to be about 3.7 tonnes per hectare. What is the yield from a rectangular field measuring 143 metres by 208 metres?

Exercise 10I   Mixed questions

1   Find the area of the triangles shown:
    (a)   (b)

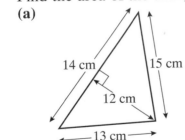

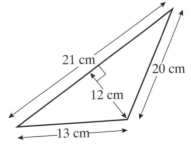

2   Work out the area of the bath mats shown:
    (a)   (b)

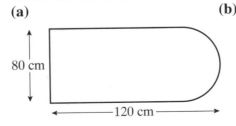

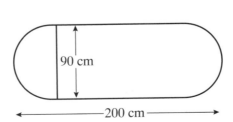

3 The diagram shows a skateboard ramp. The curved surface has two edges which are quarter circles. Work out the area of the curved surface.

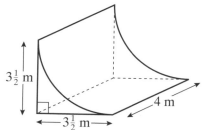

4 Work out the volume and surface area of this wedge. The curved edges are quarter circles.

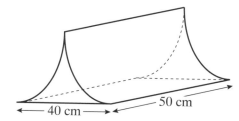

5 Work out the volume and surface area of this loaf of bread:

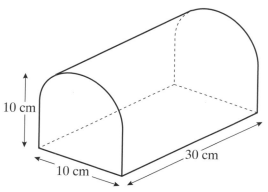

6 In this question the measurements are mixed, using mm, cm, and m. They are planks of wood. Copy and complete the table:

Thickness	Length	Width	Volume
12 mm	1.8 m	5 cm	
9 mm	2.4 m	8 cm	
15 mm	3.0 m		9000 cm³
5 cm		5 cm	0.02 m³

Summary of key points

- The area of a triangle is $\frac{1}{2}$ base × height or $\frac{1}{2}bh$.
- The area of a parallelogram is base × perpendicular height.
- The area of a trapezium is $\frac{1}{2}h(a + b)$.
- The area of a circle is πr^2.

■ Cuboid: surface area $= 2(ab + bc + ac)$
             volume $= abc$

■ The volume of a prism is base area × height.

■ The surface area of a cylinder is $2\pi rh + 2\pi r^2$.

■ The volume of a cylinder is $\pi r^2 h$.

■ You are expected to know these equivalents:
1 kg = 2.2 pounds (lb)
8 kilometres = 5 miles
1 litre = 1.75 pints
30 cm = 1 foot
2.54 cm = 1 inch
4.5 litres = 1 gallon

11 Handling data: processing data 1

11.1 Scatter diagrams

- Scatter diagrams can be drawn to show whether two sets of data are related.
- If the points on a scatter diagram are very nearly along a straight line then there is high correlation between the variables.
- Positive (or direct) correlation occurs when as one quantity increases the other one also increases.
- Negative (or inverse) correlation occurs when as one quantity increases the other quantity decreases.
- If the points are scattered randomly about there is no correlation.
- A line which is drawn to pass as close as possible to all the plotted points on a scatter diagram is called *a line of best fit*.

Example 1

The table provides information about the ages and values of ten used cars:

Age (years)	Value (£1000)
3	5.5
6	2.4
8	1.3
2	8
2	7.5
1	10.4
4	4.6
5	4
6	3.9
1	9

(a) Plot these points on a scatter diagram.
(b) Comment on the relationship between the ages and the values of the cars.
(c) Draw a line of best fit.
(d) Use your line of best fit to
    (i) estimate the value of a car aged 7 years,
    (ii) estimate the age of a car valued at £7200.

(a)   The plot of the points is shown here:

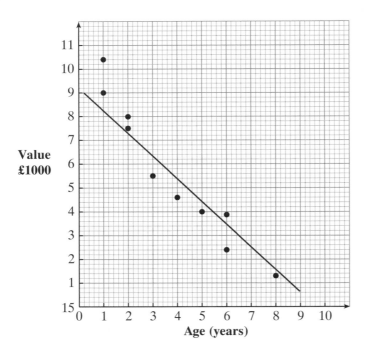

Note: in the examination Higher Tier candidates are unlikely to be asked to plot the points on a scatter diagram, but it is included here for completeness.

(b)   The scatter diagram shows negative correlation.
(c)   The line of best fit is drawn as here:
(d)   (i)   The estimate for the value of a car aged 7 years is £2500.
     (ii)   The estimate for the age of a car valued at £7200 is 2 years.

Exercise 11A   **Links (*4G, 4H*) 4G, 4H**

1   The table shows the marks scored in a Mathematics test and a Science test:

Maths	26	41	40	39	44	41	25	40	33	37
Science	20	39	38	40	40	39	28	44	30	39

    (a)   Plot these points on a scatter diagram.
    (b)   Draw the line of best fit.
    (c)   Comment on the correlation between the two sets of marks.
    (d)   Estimate the mark likely to be gained in the Science test by a student who gained a mark of 36 in the Maths test.

2 The scatter diagram provides information about the number of units of electricity used in heating a house on ten different days and the average temperature for each day:

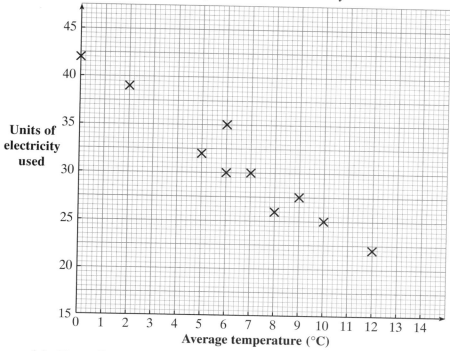

(a) Describe the correlation between the number of units of electricity used and the average temperature.

(b) Copy the diagram and draw a line of best fit.

(c) Use your line of best fit to estimate
    (i) the average temperature if 33 units of electricity are used,
    (ii) the units of electricity used if the average temperature is 4 °C.

3 The scatter graph shows information about 12 countries. For each country, it shows the birth rate and life expectancy in years.

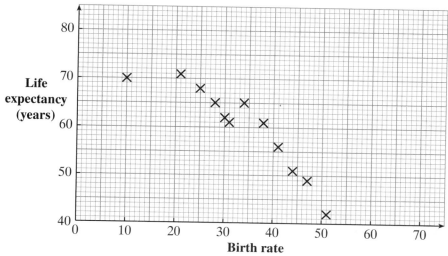

(a) Comment on the relationship between birth rate and life expectancy.
(b) Copy the scatter diagram and draw the line of best fit.
(c) Use your line of best fit to estimate the life expectancy in a country with a birth rate of 43.

11.2 Grouped data

■ An estimate of the mean for grouped data is

$$\bar{x} = \frac{\Sigma fx}{\Sigma f}$$

where f is the frequency and x is the mid-point of the class interval.

■ The modal class interval is the interval with the highest frequency.

■ The class interval containing the median will be the class interval which contains the middle value if the values are placed in order.

■ To be able to compare two statistical distributions fully you need a measure of 'average', such as the mean, and a measure of spread.

Teaching reference:
(*pp 265–277, sections 15.1– 15.4; pp 287–291, sections 15.6, 15.7*)
pp 305–314, sections 15.1, 15.2, 15.3; pp 326–330, section 15.6

Example 2

The ages of 50 members of an aerobics class are given below:

Age (a) in years	Frequency
$10 < a \leqslant 20$	4
$20 < a \leqslant 30$	18
$30 < a \leqslant 40$	10
$40 < a \leqslant 50$	15
$50 < a \leqslant 60$	3

(a) Write down the modal class interval for the ages.
(b) Write down the class interval containing the median age.
(c) Work out an estimate for the mean of the ages.
(d) Work out the maximum possible range for the ages.

The swimming club has 50 members. The mean of their ages is 25 years.

(e) Explain why it is not possible to say that on the whole the members of the swimming club are younger than the members of the aerobics class. You may illustrate your answer with an example.

(a) The interval with the largest frequency is $20 < a \leqslant 30$. This is the modal class interval.

(b) If we placed the ages from youngest to oldest then, potentially, they would range from 10 (or just over) to 60 years. For the median we require the middle age in this list – so we would require the 25th number along this list. There are 22 ages up to 30 years so the 25th age will be in the interval $30 < a \leqslant 40$. So the class interval containing the median is $30 < a \leqslant 40$.

(c) For the estimated mean, we replace each class interval with its mid-point, i.e. for $10 < a \leqslant 20$ the mid-point is 15.

Mid-point	Frequency	Mid-point × frequency
15	4	$15 \times 4 = 60$
25	18	$25 \times 18 = 450$
35	10	$35 \times 10 = 350$
45	15	$45 \times 15 = 675$
55	3	$55 \times 3 = 165$
Total	50	Total $= 1700$

So the estimated mean age is $\frac{1700}{50} = 34$ years.

(d) The range of the ages = oldest age – youngest age.
We cannot be certain about either the oldest or youngest, but we do know that the youngest could be (just over) 10 years and the oldest could be 60.
So the maximum range could be $60 - 10 = 50$ years.

(e) Superficially, because the mean age of the swimmers is lower than the mean age at the aerobics class, it might look as if the swimmers are, on the whole, younger. However, we do not have the range of ages for the swimmers so we simply cannot arrive at any sensible comparison. For instance the 50 swimmers could be made up as follows:

20 aged 10 and 30 aged 35

This gives a mean age of

$$\frac{20 \times 10 + 30 \times 35}{50} = \frac{1250}{50} = 25$$

But it would be silly to say that the swimmers are, in general, younger than the people at the aerobics class when, in fact, 30 of the swimmers (over half of them) would be older than the mean age of the aerobics class.

1   A bag contains 40 potatoes. The distribution of weights of the potatoes is given in the table below:

Weight (*w*) g	Frequency
$0 < w \leqslant 100$	2
$100 < w \leqslant 200$	16
$200 < w \leqslant 300$	10
$300 < w \leqslant 400$	9
$400 < w \leqslant 500$	3

     (a) Work out an estimate for the mean weight of the potatoes in the bag.

     (b) Write down the class interval which contains the median weight.

     (c) Write down the modal class interval.
          A second bag of 40 has in it potatoes with a mean weight of exactly 250 g.

     (d) Is it possible to say, in general, that the potatoes in the second bag have a weight which is either greater or smaller than those in the first bag?

2   A survey was conducted of the speeds of 80 vehicles on a main road at lunchtime. The results of the survey are shown below:

Speed (*s*) in mph	Frequency
$0 < s \leqslant 10$	1
$10 < s \leqslant 20$	2
$20 < s \leqslant 30$	10
$30 < s \leqslant 40$	30
$40 < s \leqslant 50$	32
$50 < s \leqslant 60$	3
$60 < s \leqslant 70$	2

     (a) Work out the estimate of the mean speed of these vehicles.

     (b) Write down the modal class interval for the speed.

     (c) Write down the class interval which contains the median.

   The speed limit on the road is 45 mph.

     (d) Estimate how many of the vehicles in the survey were exceeding the speed limit. Give your reasons.

A second survey was conducted on the same road at midnight. For this second survey the mean speed of the vehicles was found to be 43 mph. A report on the two surveys concluded that

'on the whole people tend to drive faster at midnight than at lunchtime'.

(e) Comment on the correctness or otherwise of this conclusion.

3 75 students took a test with a maximum possible mark of 30. The number of marks scored by the students are grouped in the frequency table below:

Marks scored	Number of students
1 to 5	10
6 to 10	15
11 to 15	14
16 to 20	7
21 to 25	9
26 to 30	20

(a) Write down the modal class interval.
(b) Work out the class interval which contains the median.
(c) Work out an estimate for the mean number of marks scored.

11.3 Time series and moving averages

- A graph showing how a given value changes over time is called a *time series*.
- Seasonal variations in time series can be smoothed out using a moving average.

Example 3

The table below provides information about the number of job vacancies shown at the job centre in the district of Ashwell during periods from 1999 to 2001.

Year	March	June	September	December
1999	783	885	845	521
2000	721	820	850	482
2001	650	740	763	470

(a) Plot the information as a time series.
(b) Work out the 4-point moving averages for the data.
(c) Use your time series and moving averages to help comment on whether or not there is evidence to suggest that the number of job vacancies in Ashwell fell during the period from early 1999 to late 2001.

(a)

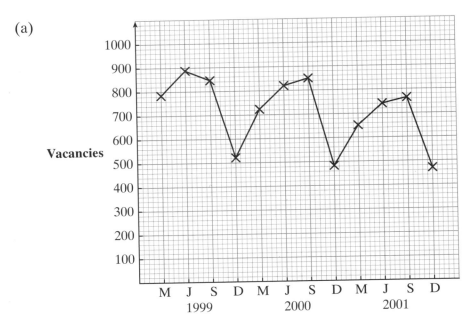

(b) The 4-point moving averages are $\dfrac{783 + 885 + 845 + 521}{4} = 758.5$

then $\dfrac{885 + 845 + 521 + 721}{4} = 743$ then $\dfrac{845 + 521 + 721 + 820}{4} = 726.75$, etc.

The full set of moving averages is as follows:

1st	2nd	3rd	4th	5th	6th	7th	8th	9th
758.5	743	726.75	728	718.25	700.5	680.5	658.75	655.75

If we now plot these moving averages against time we have

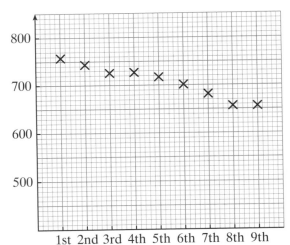

The graph clearly indicates that the number of job vacancies fell between early 1999 and late 2001.

Example 4

The table below gives information about the quarterly heating bill for Steve's flat.

Year	Jan to March	April to June	July to Sept	Oct to Dec
1998	£201	£118	£60	£182
1999	£210	£127	£63	£191
2000	£223	£131	£64	£198
2001	£232	£140	£66	£203

(a) Plot this information as a time series.

(b) Work out the four-point moving averages for these heating bills.

(c) Plot the moving averages as points on a scatter diagram.

(d) Comment on your results.

(a) The graph of the time series is

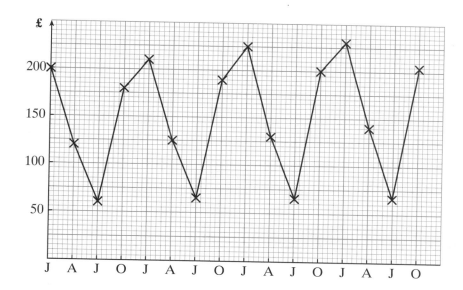

(b) The moving averages are

$$\frac{201 + 118 + 60 + 182}{4} = £140.25$$

$$\frac{118 + 60 + 182 + 210}{4} = £142.5$$

etc, to give a complete set (in £s) as:

1st	2nd	3rd	4th	5th	6th	7th	8th	9th	10th	11th	12th	13th
140.25	142.5	144.75	145.5	147.75	151	152	152.25	154	156.25	158.5	159	160.25

(c) The scatter diagram is

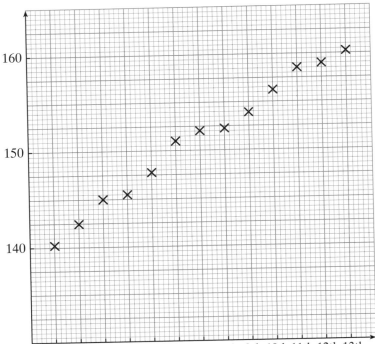

(d) The time series indicates that:
- the heating costs are at their lowest during the summer months of July, August and September
- the heating costs are at their highest during the winter months of January, February and March

whilst the scatter diagram indicates that there is a general trend upwards in heating bills.

Exercise 11C   Links 15B

1   Jon works as a sales representative. On top of his salary he is paid a bonus according to the number of sales he makes. The bonus is paid three times a year.

The table below provides information about Jon's bonus payments from April 1998 up to December 2001:

Year	April	August	December
1998	£400	£390	£600
1999	£380	£420	£635
2000	£410	£380	£640
2001	£425	£435	£650

(a) Plot this information as a time series.
(b) Work out the 3-point moving averages for the data and plot these as a graph.
(c) Comment on whether or not there is evidence to suggest that Jon's bonus payments have risen or fallen over the period from April 1998 to December 2001.

2 The number of issues of videos from a shop during the year 2000 is given below:

Month	Jan	Feb	Mar	April	May	June	July	Aug	Sept	Oct	Nov	Dec
Number	124	132	125	118	120	98	82	76	110	130	142	128

(a) Plot the information as a time series.
(b) Work out the 4-point moving averages and plot these as a graph.
(c) Comment on the variation shown in the data.

3 Crestline Company recorded their quarterly turnover for each quarter from 1998 to 2001.
The results are given below, the turnover being in millions of pounds.

	1998	1999	2000	2001
1st quarter	1.8	2.0	2.1	2.3
2nd quarter	1.4	1.8	2.0	2.1
3rd quarter	1.2	1.5	1.8	2.0
4th quarter	1.9	1.8	2.0	2.1

(a) Plot the information as a time series.
(b) Work out the 4-point moving averages and plot these as a graph.
(c) Comment on how the company's turnover has changed over the years from 1998 to 2001 inclusive.

4 Sandra works as a sales representative. At the end of April, August and December each year she receives a bonus payment. The bonus depends upon the number of sales she has made.
The table below shows figures for Sandra's bonus payments over a five year period.

Year	April	August	December
1996	£702	£344	£954
1997	£773	£371	£1001
1998	£842	£411	£1098
1999	£903	£460	£1200
2000	£1006	£512	£1345

(a) Plot this information as a time series.

(b) Work out the set of 3-point moving averages for Sandra's bonus payments.

(c) Plot the moving averages on a scatter diagram.

(d) Comment on the results.

Summary of key points

- Scatter diagrams can be drawn to show whether two sets of data are related.

- If the points on a scatter diagram are very nearly along a straight line then there is high correlation between the variables.

- Positive (or direct) correlation occurs when as one quantity increases the other one also increases.

- Negative (or inverse) correlation occurs when as one quantity increases the other quantity decreases.

- If the points are scattered randomly about there is no correlation.

- A line which is drawn to pass as close as possible to all the plotted points on a scatter diagram is called a *a line of best fit*.

- An estimate of the mean for grouped data is

$$\bar{x} = \frac{\Sigma fx}{\Sigma f}$$

  where f is the frequency and x is the mid-point of the class interval.

- The modal class interval is the interval with the highest frequency.

- The class interval containing the median will be the class interval which contains the middle value if the values are placed in order.

- To be able to compare two statistical distributions fully you need a measure of 'average', such as the mean, and a measure of spread.

- A graph showing how a given value changes over time is called a *time series*.

- Seasonal variations in time series can be smoothed out using a moving average.

12 Handling data: processing data 2

12.1 Cumulative frequency curves

Teaching reference:
(*pp 74–80, section 4.8;*
pp 277–286, section 15.5)
pp 79–85, section 4.8;
pp 318–326, section 15.5

The cumulative frequency curve for grouped data is used to estimate the median, some measures of spread and various proportions of the data.

- ■ **The median is the middle value of the distribution.**
- ■ **The lower quartile is the value one-quarter of the way into the distribution.**
- ■ **The upper quartile is the value three-quarters of the way into the distribution.**
- ■ **Interquartile range = upper quartile − lower quartile**
- ■ **The cumulative frequency curve can be used to find the percentage or proportion of the whole distribution lying between two values.**
- ■ **To compare two distributions you should use a measure of average and a measure of spread.**
- ■ **A box plot is a diagrammatic way of showing the median, the upper quartile and the lower quartile.**
- ■ **Box plots are very useful when you wish to compare two or more distributions.**

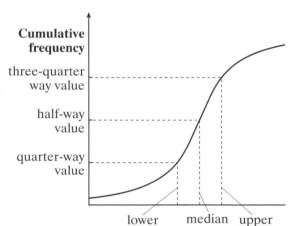

Example 1

There are 150 members of Vijay's sports club.
The ages of the members are grouped and set out in this table:
(a) Construct a cumulative frequency table.
(b) Draw the cumulative frequency curve.
(c) Use the curve to estimate the median age of the members.
(d) Use the curve to estimate the interquartile range of the ages.
(e) Estimate the percentage of members aged between 23 and 46 years.
(f) Construct a box plot for this distribution.

Age (*a*) in years	Frequency
$0 < a \leqslant 10$	6
$10 < a \leqslant 20$	20
$20 < a \leqslant 30$	24
$30 < a \leqslant 40$	33
$40 < a \leqslant 50$	28
$50 < a \leqslant 60$	22
$60 < a \leqslant 70$	12
$70 < a \leqslant 80$	5

The median age of the members of Tina's sports club is 43 years.
The upper and lower quartiles of the ages at Tina's sports club are 58 and 20 years respectively.

(g) Compare as fully as possible the distribution of ages at the two sports clubs.

(a) The cumulative frequency table is

Age	Cumulative frequency
Up to 10	6
Up to 20	26
Up to 30	50
Up to 40	83
Up to 50	111
Up to 60	133
Up to 70	145
Up to 80	150

(b) The cumulative frequency curve is

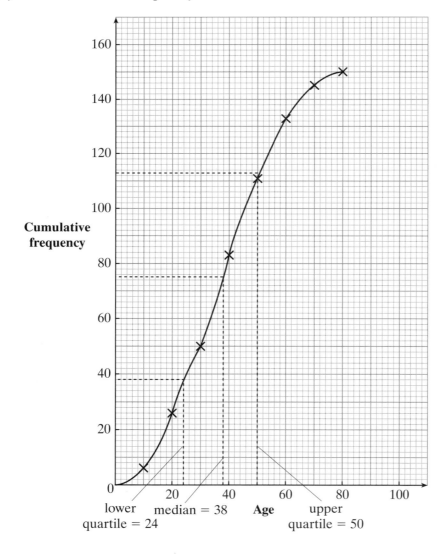

(c) From the curve the estimate of the median age is 38 years.
(d) The upper and lower quartiles are 50 and 24 respectively. So interquartile range = 50 − 24 = 26 years
(e)

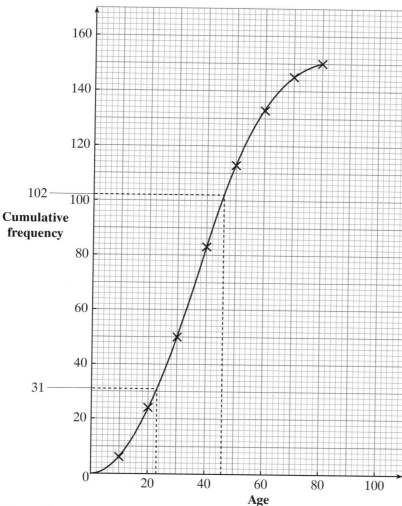

The estimates are that

there are 31 members with an age up to 23
there are 102 members with an age up to 46

So the estimate for the number of members aged between 23 and 46 is

$$102 - 31 = 71$$

As a % of 150, 71 is

$$\frac{71}{150} \times 100 = 47\tfrac{1}{3}\%$$

(f) The box plot for the distribution is

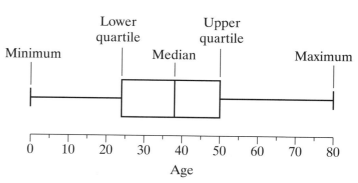

(g) Comparing the two distributions using box plots:

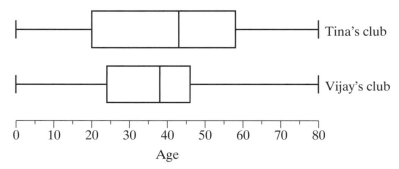

The median age at Tina's club is greater than the median age at Vijay's. However the interquartile range at Tina's is greater than that at Vijay's.

In consequence there could be a significant number of members at Tina's club younger than the lower quartile age at Vijay's club, or many more older than the upper quartile age at Vijay's club.

The consequence is that we cannot make any definite statement about which club has the older membership overall.

Example 2

Sketch the cumulative frequency curve for the distribution represented by each of these histograms:

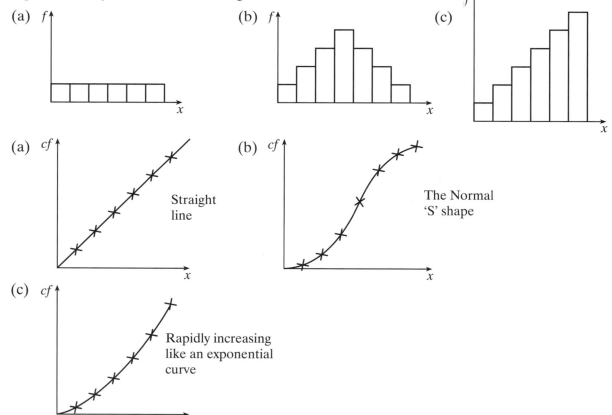

Exercise 12A   **Links** (*4F, 15D*) **4F, 15E**

1   75 students at Streetfield School took part in a darts
competition. Each student threw darts until they hit a
bull's-eye. The number of darts thrown by the students are
grouped in the frequency table.

Number of darts thrown	Frequency
1 to 5	10
6 to 10	17
11 to 15	11
16 to 20	5
21 to 25	12
26 to 30	20

(a) Construct a cumulative frequency table.
(b) Draw a cumulative frequency curve.
(c) Use your cumulative frequency curve to find estimates for
    (i)   the median number of darts thrown,
    (ii)   the upper and lower quartiles for the number of
        darts thrown,
    (iii) the interquartile range of the number of darts
        thrown,
    (iv)   the proportion of students who took between 12 and
        24 darts to hit a bull's-eye.
(d) Draw a box plot for this distribution.

A similar darts competition was held at Harwell School. In this
competition the median number of darts to hit a bull's-eye was
12 and the upper and lower quartiles were 18 and 9 respectively.

(e) Comment as fully as possible on the quality of dart
    throwing in the two competitions.

2   At a dentist's, the receptionist recorded the lengths of time
that 80 patients had to wait before being checked in.
The waiting times were as follows:

Waiting time (*t*) seconds	Frequency
$0 < t \leqslant 60$	4
$60 < t \leqslant 120$	8
$120 < t \leqslant 180$	10
$180 < t \leqslant 240$	18
$240 < t \leqslant 300$	30
$300 < t \leqslant 360$	10

(a) Construct a cumulative frequency table.
(b) Draw a cumulative frequency curve.
(c) Use the curve to estimate
    (i) the median waiting time,
    (ii) the interquartile range of the waiting times.
(d) Draw a box plot for the waiting times.

3 The grouped frequency table gives information about the weekly rainfall at Gatwick airport during the year 2000:

Weekly rainfall (m) in mm	Frequency
$0 < m \leqslant 10$	18
$10 < m \leqslant 20$	20
$20 < m \leqslant 30$	6
$30 < m \leqslant 40$	3
$40 < m \leqslant 50$	3
$50 < m \leqslant 60$	2

(a) Construct a cumulative frequency table.
(b) Draw a cumulative frequency curve.
(c) Estimate the median weekly rainfall at Gatwick airport during 2000.
(d) Estimate the interquartile range of the rainfall.
(e) Estimate the number of weeks during the year 2000 when the weekly rainfall at Gatwick airport was greater than 15 mm.

During the year 2000 the weekly rainfall at Manchester airport had a median of 22 mm with upper and lower quartiles of 9 mm and 30 mm.

(f) Comment as fully as possible about the difference in weekly rainfall at the two airports during the year 2000.

4 A sample of 80 girls and 80 boys was made for a survey into the relative weights of the girls and boys. The results of the enquiry are represented on the joint cumulative frequency diagram below.

(a) Make three valid statistical comparisons based on the diagram.
(b) Draw parallel box plots for the two distributions.
(c) Work out an estimate for the percentage of girls
    (i) heavier than the upper quartile weight for the boys
    (ii) lighter than the lower 15th percentile of the weight for the boys.

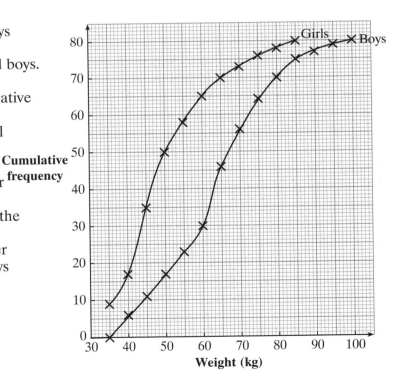

5 A group of 80 students took an examination in Science and an examination in Geography. Both examinations had a total of 100 marks.

The diagrams below represent the box plots for the distribution of marks.

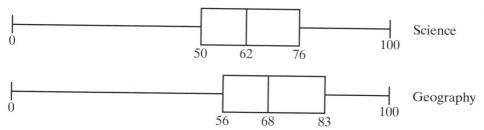

Comment as fully as possible on the relative difficulties of these two examinations.

6 The diagram below represents a box plot for the distribution of ages of people in the village of Champling. A total of 400 people live in the village.
Sketch the cumulative frequency curve for the ages of the people in the village.

12.2 Histograms

■ **A histogram can be drawn for equal class widths.**

■ **A histogram can be drawn for unequal class widths.**

■ **When unequal class widths are used the vertical axis is the frequency density.**

■ **Frequency density** $= \dfrac{\text{frequency}}{\text{class width}}$ **but this value can be scaled up or down so that the histogram adequately fits the page.**

■ **For any histogram the areas of the rectangles are proportional to the frequencies they represent.**

Teaching reference:
(pp 527–541, sections 29.1, 29.2)
pp 548–560, sections 27.1, 27.2

Example 3

A sack contains 160 letters.

The incomplete frequency table provides some information about the masses of these letters.

The incomplete histogram also provides some information about the masses of the letters.

Mass (m) grams	Frequency
$0 < m \leqslant 100$	10
$100 < m \leqslant 150$	
$150 < m \leqslant 200$	42
$200 < m \leqslant 250$	50
$250 < m \leqslant 400$	

(a) Use the frequency table to complete the histogram.
(b) Use the histogram to complete the frequency table.

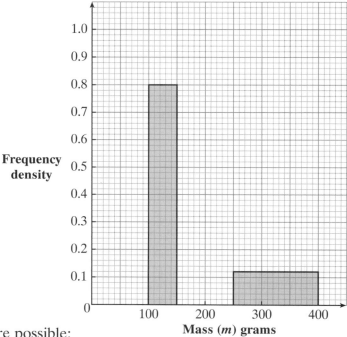

(a) Work out the frequency density where possible:

Mass	Frequency	Frequency density
$0 < m \leqslant 100$	10	$10 \div 100 = 0.1$
$150 < m \leqslant 200$	42	$42 \div 50 = 0.84$
$200 < m \leqslant 250$	50	$50 \div 50 = 1$

So we can now complete the histogram as shown:

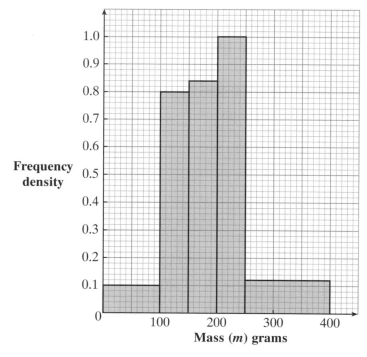

(b) From the histogram, the frequency density for the interval
$100 < m \leqslant 150 = 0.8$. So the frequency for this class is

frequency = frequency density × class width
$$= 0.8 \times 50 = 40$$

And for the interval $250 < m \leqslant 400$, the frequency
density $= 0.12$, so

$$\text{frequency} = 0.12 \times 150 = 18$$

So the complete table is

Mass (m) in grams	Frequency
$0 < m \leqslant 100$	10
$100 < m \leqslant 150$	**40**
$150 < m \leqslant 200$	42
$200 < m \leqslant 250$	50
$250 < m \leqslant 400$	**18**

Exercise 12B   Links (29A) 27A

1   There were a number of advertisements advertising cars for sale
    last Friday. The incomplete table provides some information
    about the prices of these cars. Information about the prices of
    the cars also appears in the incomplete histogram.

Students should choose
their own scale and axes.

Price (p) in £	Frequency
$0 < p \leqslant 1000$	
$1000 < p \leqslant 3000$	36
$3000 < p \leqslant 6000$	48
$6000 < p \leqslant 8000$	
$8000 < p \leqslant 10\,000$	20
$10\,000 < p \leqslant 15\,000$	

(a) Use the information in the
    table to complete the histogram.
(b) Use the histogram to complete
    the table.

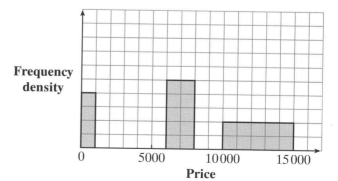

2   Mr Jones asks some students how long they spent on homework last night. The unfinished histogram and frequency table provide information about their responses:

Homework time (*t*) minutes	Frequency
$20 < t \leqslant 25$	20
$25 < t \leqslant 40$	
$40 < t \leqslant 60$	
$60 < t \leqslant 85$	
$85 < t \leqslant 90$	6

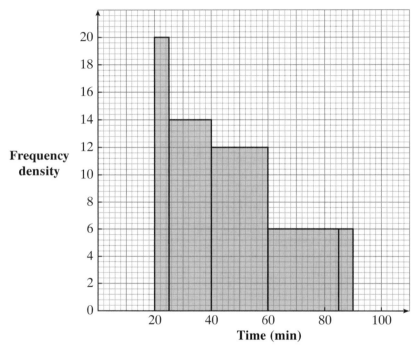

No student spent less than 20 minutes on their homework. No student spent more than 90 minutes on their homework.
(a) Use the histogram to complete the table.
(b) Work out the number of students asked by Mr Jones.

3   The table shows the distribution of weights of a group of 40 people:

Draw a histogram for this distribution.

Weight (*W*) kg	Frequency
$0 < W \leqslant 30$	3
$30 < W \leqslant 50$	9
$50 < W \leqslant 60$	16
$60 < W \leqslant 70$	9
$70 < W \leqslant 100$	3

12.3 Some general principles related to data

Teaching reference:
(pp 69–72, section 4.6)

- Data may be either primary or secondary.
- Whether you collect primary or secondary data you need to make sure that the selection is free from bias.
- There may be times when you need to consider the implications of missing or possibly rogue data.
- Calculators will perform specific statistical functions.

Example 4

Sally has undertaken a project looking at the relative heights of 50 boys and 50 girls.
Some of her results are represented on the joint cumulative frequency diagram below.

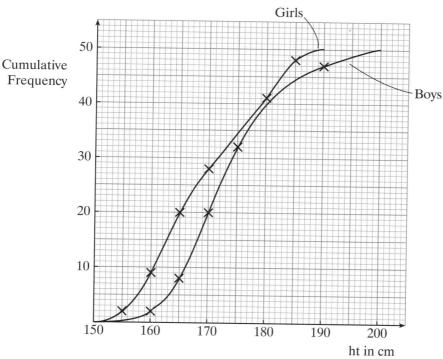

(a) Make **three** valid statistical conclusions based on these graphs. Give your reasons in each case.

(b) Work out an estimate of the percentage of girls taller than:
  (i) the median height for the boys
  (ii) the upper quartile of the boys' height
  (iii) the 90th percentile of the boys height.

Answer

(a) three valid conclusions are:
- In general the girls are not as tall as the boys. This can be seen because the cumulative frequency curve for the girls is to the left of that for the boys.

- The range of heights for the girls is $190 - 150 = 140$ cm whilst that for the boys is $200 - 155 = 44$ cm.
- The median height for the girls is 168 cm whilst that for the boys is 172 cm.

(b) **(i)** The median height for the boys is 172 cm.

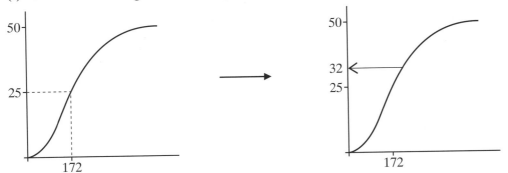

Transferring that height to the cumulative frequency diagram for the girls shows that we can estimate that 32 girls have a height up to 172 cm, so there are an estimated 18 girls out of 50, or:

$$\frac{18}{50} = 36\%$$

of the girls taller than the median height of the boys.

(b) **(ii)** The upper quartile for the boys' height is 178 cm.

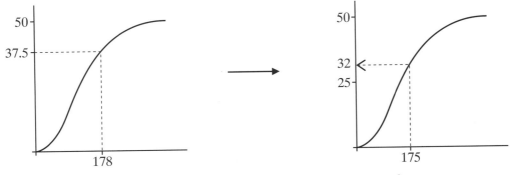

Transferring this height to the cumulative frequency curve for the girls:

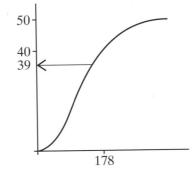

suggests that 39 of the 50 girls have a height up to 178 cm, so 11 out of 50, or 22% of the girls have a height greater than the upper quartile height for the boys.

(b) **(iii)** Finally, the 90th percentile height for the boys is 187 cm.

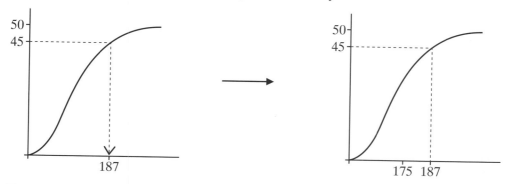

Transferring this height to the cumulative frequency diagram for the girls indicates that only one girl out of 50, or 2%, are taller than the 90th percentile for the boys.

Exercise 12C   Links (*4D*)

1   You are conducting a survey into the word length used in two magazines. Write down the steps you would take to ensure that you made a random sample of at least 50 words from each magazine.

2   In doing a survey into the relationship between value and age of some second-hand cars you plot data on a scatter diagram. The diagram looks like this:

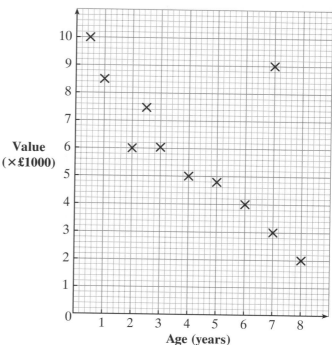

There is clearly a rogue point; an outlier which goes against the trend. What are your reasonable alternatives in a situation such as this?

3   Use the $\bar{X}$ button on your calculator to work out the mean of the numbers

  3, 7, 8, 5, 9, 10, 7, 8, 6, 2.

Check your result without using the calculator.

Summary of key points

- The median is the middle value of the distribution.
- The lower quartile is the value one-quarter of the way into the distribution.
- The upper quartile is the value three-quarters of the way into the distribution.
- Interquartile range = upper quartile − lower quartile
- The cumulative frequency curve can be used to find the percentage or proportion of the whole distribution lying between two values.
- To compare two distributions you should use a measure of average and a measure of spread.
- A box plot is a diagrammatic way of showing the median, the upper quartile and the lower quartile.
- Box plots are very useful when you wish to compare two or more distributions.
- A histogram can be drawn for equal class widths.
- A histogram can be drawn for unequal class widths.
- When unequal class widths are used the vertical axis is the frequency density.
- Frequency density $= \dfrac{\text{frequency}}{\text{class width}}$ but this value can be scaled up or down so that the histogram adequately fits the page.
- For any histogram the areas of the rectangles are proportional to the frequencies they represent.
- Data may be either primary or secondary.
- Whether you collect primary or secondary data you need to make sure that the selection is free from bias.
- There may be times when you need to consider the implications of missing or possibly rogue data.
- Calculators will perform specific statistical functions.

Examination style practice paper

Section 1 **You must not use a calculator.**

1

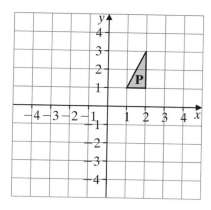

Rotate triangle **P** through 180° about the point with coordinates $(-1, 1)$. Label the image **Q**. (2)

2 Here are four patterns of dots:

Pattern number 1   Pattern number 2

Pattern number 3   Pattern number 4

(a) Find an expression for the number of dots in pattern number n. (2)

(b) Find the pattern number of the pattern with 50 dots. (1)

3 Work out $5\frac{2}{3} - 3\frac{4}{5}$. (3)

4 **(a)** Simplify $\dfrac{c^3}{c^7}$. (1)

(b) Multiply $3p^3q^5 \times 4p^2q$. Give your answer as simply as possible. (2)

5

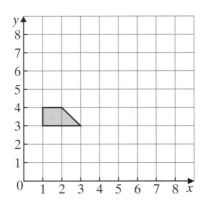

On the grid, enlarge the shaded shape by a scale factor of -2 from $(3, 4)$. (2)

6 The histogram shows information about the time, in minutes, for which the students in a class paid attention in a half-hour lesson.

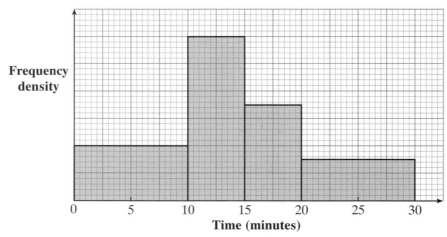

12 students had an attention time greater than or equal to 10 minutes and less than 15 minutes.

Use the information in the histogram to complete this frequency table:

Time (t) in minutes	Frequency
$0 \leqslant t < 10$	
$10 \leqslant t < 15$	12
$15 \leqslant t < 20$	
$20 \leqslant t < 30$	

(3)

7 Given that $8^{\frac{3}{2}} \times 4^{\frac{1}{4}} = 2^n$, find the value of n. (3)

Section 2 You may use a calculator.

1   Chris scored 51 out of 75 in a test.
    Express 51 out of 75 as a percentage.   (2)

2

Month	January	February	March	April
Income	£947	£2348	£1742	£3131

The table shows Mary's income in each of the first four
months of last year.
Calculate the two 3-month moving averages for her income in
this period.   (2)

3   Expand and simplify
    (a) $x(3x^2 + 4)$,   (2)
    (b) $5(3x + 2) - 3(5x - 1)$.   (2)

4

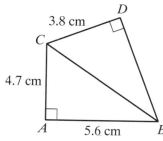

9.7 cm

Diagram NOT
drawn accurately.

$a°$

7.8 cm

Calculate the size of the angle marked $a°$.
Give your answer correct to 1 decimal place.   (3)

5   Solve the equation $\dfrac{1 - 5x}{2} = 5 - x$.   (3)

6

D

3.8 cm

C

Diagram NOT
drawn accurately.

4.7 cm

A 5.6 cm B

Triangle ABC is right-angled at A.
$AB = 5.6$ cm and $AC = 4.7$ cm.
Triangle BCD is right-angled at D.
$CD = 3.8$ cm.

Calculate the length of BD.
Give your answer correct to 3 significant figures.   (5)

Answers

Exercise 1A

1 (a) $2^2 \times 3^2$ (b) $2^3 \times 5^2$
(c) 3×5^2 (d) $3^3 \times 5^2$
(e) $2^2 \times 7^2$ (f) $2^2 \times 3^3$
(g) $2^2 \times 11 \times 13$ (h) $2^4 \times 7^2$
(i) $2^3 \times 11^2$ (j) $2^5 \times 3^2 \times 7$
(k) $7^2 \times 11^2$ (l) $2^2 \times 7^2 \times 11$
(m) $2^5 \times 3^2$ (n) $2^6 \times 5^3$
(o) $2^4 \times 5^2 \times 19$

2 (a) HCF = 12, LCM = 72
(b) HCF = 15, LCM = 75
(c) HCF = 5, LCM = 180
(d) HCF = 9, LCM = 270
(e) HCF = 70, LCM = 420
(f) HCF = 7, LCM = 210
(g) HCF = 5, LCM = 420
(h) HCF = 14, LCM = 980
(i) HCF = 21, LCM = 630
(j) HCF = 16, LCM = 96

Exercise 1B

1 (a) $2^{10} = 1024$ (b) $3^{12} = 531\,441$
(c) $5^8 = 390\,625$ (d) $4^7 = 16\,384$
(e) $2^{12} = 4096$ (f) $3^6 = 729$
(g) $7^3 = 343$ (h) $6^1 = 6$
(i) $11^4 = 14\,641$ (j) $4^0 = 1$

2 (a) x^5 (b) x^9
(c) y^5 (d) y^6
(e) $6x^7$ (f) $12y^7$
(g) $2y^2$ (h) $4k$
(i) x^3y^5 (j) a^4b^3
(k) p^6q^4 (l) xy^3
(m) p^2 (n) $2a^4b^2$
(o) a^3b^4 (p) $2ab$
(q) $(x+y)^5$ (r) $(2xy+y)^2$

Exercise 1C

1 (a) 3×10^4, 4×10^2, 6×10^{-3}, 8×10^{-5}
(b) 2.17×10^3, 6.3×10^1, 7.1×10^4, 7.61×10^{-1}
(c) 2.03×10^2, 5.003×10^4, 9.01×10^{-3}, 1.01×10^{-2}

2 (a) 310   (b) 26 000
(c) 89   (d) 0.67
(e) 0.001 57   (f) 0.000 204
(g) 100.3   (h) 30.6
(i) 0.007 0103   (j) 0.040 79

3 (a) 300   (b) 30 000
(c) 90   (d) 0.7
(e) 0.002   (f) 0.0002
(g) 100   (h) 30
(i) 0.007   (j) 0.04

Exercise 1D

1 $8\frac{1}{4}$ **2** 35   **3** 8
4 $3\frac{3}{5}$ **5** $3\frac{3}{7}$ **6** $10\frac{1}{4}$
7 24   **8** 3   **9** 7
10 $3\frac{4}{5}$ **11** 2   **12** $1\frac{1}{2}$
13 $2\frac{1}{4}$ **14** $\frac{5}{8}$ **15** 28
16 $\frac{5}{12}$ **17** $2\frac{1}{7}$ **18** $\frac{7}{8}$

Exercise 1E

1 (a) 0.375   (b) 0.109 375
(c) 0.68   (d) 0.776
(e) 0.3472   (f) 0.2916
(g) $0.2\dot{4}$ (h) $0.\dot{5}3846\dot{1}$
(i) $0.13\dot{6}$ (j) $0.6\dot{3}$
(k) $0.27\dot{1}$ (l) $0.358\,974$

2 (a) $\frac{1}{9}$ (b) $\frac{7}{11}$ (c) $\frac{14}{45}$
(d) $\frac{8}{37}$ (e) $\frac{5}{11}$ (f) $\frac{146}{1111}$
(g) $\frac{49}{333}$ (h) $\frac{20}{27}$ (i) $\frac{6359}{9900}$
(j) $\frac{101}{180}$

Exercise 1F

1 (a) 12   (b) 640
(c) 27   (d) 3.5
(e) 40   (f) 20
(g) 10   (h) 10 000

2 (a) 300   (b) 9000
(c) 60   (d) 12
(e) 0.18   (f) 15

3 (a) 350   (b) 15
(c) 45   (d) 100
(e) 50   (f) 75

4 (a) 400, larger   (b) $2\frac{2}{3}$, larger
(c) 3, larger   (d) 12, larger

5 600 min
6 8000
7 14 000p or £140
8 160 s
9 576 000 s
10 (i) 0.6 mm
(ii) 12 mm

Exercise 2A

1 (a) 28   (b) 10.5   (c) £5.25
(d) £27.14   (e) £0.60

2 (a) 82%   (b) $112\frac{1}{2}\%$ (c) 120%
(d) $66\frac{2}{3}\%$ (e) $117\frac{1}{2}\%$

3 £6160   **4** £210
5 £20 700   **6** £110 700
7 £71 904   **8** £428.48

Exercise 2B

1 20%   **2** 4.5%   **3** 35%
4 $16\frac{2}{3}\%$ **5** $33\frac{1}{3}\%$ **6** 23%
7 9%   **8** 32%

Exercise 2C

1 £120
2 £120 000
3 £20 872 (to the nearest £)
4 261.4 g (to 1 d.p.)
5 £12.50
6 £10

Exercise 2D

1 (a) £531.50
(b) £600.58 (to nearest penny)
(c) £678.64 (to nearest penny)

2 £544.54 (nearest penny)
3 £14 599.83 (nearest penny)
4 10 yrs (after 9 yrs she is 50p short)
5 (a) $(1.035)^{25}$
(b) £94 529.80 (nearest penny)
6 41 rabbits
7 £1172.54 (nearest penny)

Exercise 2E

1 (a) $\frac{2}{5}$
(b) 140 g
2 George gets £30, Mark gets £18, John gets £12
3 (a) $\frac{1}{3}$ (b) $\frac{1}{9}$ (c) 1000
4 (a) $\frac{1}{3}$ (b) 21
5 (a) 40   (b) $\frac{2}{11}$

Exercise 2F

1 150 g of fat, 75 g of sugar
2 (a) £20   (b) £130
3 (a) 9.1 mg   (b) 18.2 mg
4 (a) $\frac{3}{20}$
(b) Pink : blue : green in ratio 5 : 12 : 3
(c) 36 blue, 9 green
5 (a) $x = 2$
(b) Douglas gets £100, Gillian gets £400

Exercise 2G

1 (a) £4   (b) £32
2 £21.30
3 (a) 100 days   (b) 25 days
4 3 days
5 10 oz flour, 5 oz butter, 2.5 oz sugar
6 $\frac{1}{3}$ hour
7 6 days
8 9 days
9 £3.04
10 $4\frac{2}{3}$ hours

Exercise 2H

1 £511.13 (nearest penny)
2 348 cm^2
3 15%
4 22% (nearest %)
5 £192.86 (nearest penny)
6 £214.87 (nearest penny)
7 $(1.015)^{50}$
8 (a) $\frac{1}{3}$ (b) £240
9 Flour 250 g, Sugar 100 g
10 (a) 2 : 3 : 4   (b) 200 ml
11 6 days
12 £3.00

Exercise 3A

1 $x = 3$ **2** $x = 7$
3 $x = 6$ **4** $x = 7$
5 $x = 16$ **6** $x = 20$
7 $x = \frac{1}{3}$ **8** $x = -3$
9 $x = 3\frac{1}{2}$ **10** $x = 0$
11 $x = -12$ **12** $x = -1\frac{2}{3}$

13 $x = 2\frac{3}{4}$ **14** $x = -4$
15 $x = 0$ **16** $x = 18$
17 $x = \frac{5}{6}$ **18** $x = 3\frac{1}{4}$
19 $x = -6$ **20** $x = -\frac{2}{3}$

Exercise 3B

1 $x = 5$ **2** $x = \frac{1}{2}$
3 $x = 6$ **4** $x = 7$
5 $x = -3$ **6** $x = 0$
7 $x = 4\frac{1}{3}$ **8** $x = \frac{3}{4}$
9 $x = 8\frac{1}{2}$ **10** $x = -2$
11 $x = -\frac{2}{3}$ **12** $x = 8$
13 $x = -4\frac{3}{4}$ **14** $x = -3$
15 $x = 2$

Exercise 3C

1 $x = 2$ **2** $x = -3$
3 $x = 3\frac{1}{4}$ **4** $x = \frac{4}{5}$
5 $x = 1\frac{1}{4}$ **6** $x = \frac{3}{10}$
7 $x = \frac{2}{3}$ **8** $x = -\frac{7}{10}$
9 $x = 2\frac{1}{2}$ **10** $x = -1\frac{1}{2}$
11 $x = 1\frac{3}{4}$ **12** $x = -\frac{1}{4}$
13 $x = 1\frac{1}{3}$ **14** $x = -\frac{1}{2}$
15 $x = 0$ **16** $x = 6$
17 $x = 1\frac{2}{5}$ **18** $x = 6$
19 $x = -1$ **20** $x = -\frac{4}{5}$

Exercise 3D

1 angle $DBE = 67°$
2 angle $PQR = 49°$
3 $48°$
4 16 cm, 17 cm, 31 cm
5 Number is 24
6 $y = 8.5$
7 Numbers are 38, 5 and 14
8 Rashid is 51
9 Length is 17 cm
10 Number is 13
11 Numbers are 17 and 29
12 Mrs Banerji is 41
13 She has 14 20p coins
14 $x = 8, y = 7$
15 Largest number is 33

Exercise 3E

1 $x = 12$ **2** $x = 24$
3 $x = 23$ **4** $x = 20$
5 $x = 11$ **6** $x = 2\frac{2}{3}$
7 $x = -4$ **8** $x = 24$
9 $x = 1\frac{1}{2}$ **10** $x = 23$
11 $x = 1\frac{1}{2}$ **12** $x = -\frac{2}{5}$
13 $x = 2\frac{1}{3}$ **14** $x = 6\frac{1}{2}$
15 $x = -2\frac{2}{3}$ **16** $x = 6\frac{3}{5}$
17 $x = -2$ **18** $x = 4$
19 $x = 2\frac{1}{2}$ **20** $x = -4\frac{1}{2}$
21 $x = 1$ **22** $x = \frac{1}{2}$
23 $x = 12$ **24** $x = 10\frac{1}{2}$
25 $x = 47$
26 $6\frac{1}{4}$
27 $x = -4$ **28** $x = -13$
29 $x = -\frac{1}{8}$ **30** $x = -4\frac{2}{5}$

Exercise 3F

1 $x = \pm 6$ **2** $x = \pm 7$
3 $x = \pm 3$ **4** $x = \pm 2$
5 $x = \pm 10$ **6** $x = \pm 2$
7 $x = \pm 4$ **8** $x = \pm\frac{4}{5}$
9 $x = \pm\frac{5}{4}$ **10** $x = \pm\frac{1}{3}$
11 $x = \pm\frac{5}{3}$ **12** $x = \pm\frac{3}{5}$
13 $x = \pm 2$ **14** $x = \pm\frac{2}{9}$
15 $x = \pm\frac{7}{5}$ **16** $x = \pm\frac{5}{2}$
17 $x = -10$ or $x = 4$ **18** $x = -4$ or $x = 14$
19 $x = -1$ or $x = 5$ **20** $x = -9$ or $x = 7$

Exercise 3G

1 $x = 9$ **2** $x = \frac{5}{8}$ **3** $x = 1\frac{3}{5}$
4 $x = \frac{1}{6}$ **5** $x = \frac{3}{10}$ **6** $x = 2\frac{1}{6}$
7 $x = 2\frac{2}{5}$ **8** $x = \frac{1}{24}$ **9** $x = 3\frac{2}{5}$
10 $x = -1\frac{1}{2}$ **11** $x = \frac{3}{4}$ **12** $x = -\frac{7}{9}$
13 $x = 3\frac{1}{6}$ **14** $x = -1$ **15** $x = 4\frac{2}{3}$
16 $x = 0$ **17** $x = 2\frac{1}{2}$ **18** $x = -\frac{2}{3}$
19 $x = \frac{1}{4}$ **20** $x = -\frac{2}{3}$

Exercise 3H

1 $x = 2.6$ (1 d.p.)   **2** $x = 3.7$ (1 d.p.)
3 $x = 1.77$ (2 d.p.)   **4** $x = 3.44$ (2 d.p.)
5 $x = 2.35$ (2 d.p.)   **6** $x = 3.76$ (2 d.p.)
7 $x = 4.55$ (2 d.p.)   **8** $x = 4.27$ (2 d.p.)
9 (a) $x = 0.158$ (3 d.p.)
  (b) $x = 4.28$ (2 d.p.)
10 $x = 4.77$ (2 d.p.)

Exercise 3I

1 $x = 2\frac{2}{3}$ **2** $x = \frac{3}{5}$
3 $x = 5\frac{3}{4}$ **4** $x = -1\frac{1}{6}$
5 $x = 1\frac{1}{2}$ **6** $x = -3$
7 $x = 3$ **8** $x = -1$
9 $x = -\frac{3}{5}$ **10** $x = \frac{2}{3}$
11 $x = 1$ **12** $x = -\frac{1}{2}$
13 $x = \frac{4}{5}$ **14** $x = -1\frac{1}{2}$
15 $x = 4\frac{4}{5}$ **16** $x = -\frac{3}{4}$
17 $x = 1$ **18** $x = \frac{1}{8}$
19 $x = -2$ **20** $x = \pm 9$
21 $x = \pm 5$ **22** $x = \pm\frac{5}{6}$
23 $x = \pm 3\frac{1}{2}$ **24** $x = \frac{5}{9}$
25 $x = 1\frac{3}{8}$ **26** $x = -\frac{1}{3}$
27 $x = -2\frac{1}{4}$
28 Equal angles are $72°$, other angle is $36°$
29 Number is 17
30 (a) $x = 4.25$ (2 d.p.)
  (b) $x = 3.51$ (2 d.p.)
  (c) $x = 3.40$ (2 d.p.)

Exercise 4A

1 $4x + 28$ **2** $9x - 18$
3 $20x + 5$ **4** $18x - 8$
5 $21 - 12x$ **6** $x^2 + 9x$
7 $x^2 - 8x$ **8** $5x^2 - 4x$
9 $2x^2 + 7x$ **10** $3x - 2x^2$
11 $-2x - 10$ **12** $-28x + 7$
13 $-30 + 5x$ **14** $16x^2 + 56x$
15 $21x^2 - 35x$ **16** $12x - 28x^2$

17 $-2x^2 - 5x$ **18** $-18x^2 - 9x$
19 $-15x^2 + 12x$ **20** $-16x - 6x^2$
21 $-28x + 4x^2$ **22** $ax + 5a$
23 $3ax - 7a$ **24** $10ax + 15a$
25 $21ax - 35a$ **26** $8a^2 - 16ax$
27 $3x^2 + 8x$ **28** $7x^2 - 5x$
29 $2x^3 + 9x^2$ **30** $5x^3 - 4x^2$

Exercise 4B

1 $6(x + 3)$ **2** $7(x - 4)$
3 $5(4x + 3)$ **4** $8(2x - 3)$
5 $a(x + 8)$ **6** $a(x - 5b)$
7 $7(2x^2 + 3)$ **8** $9(3x^2 - 2)$
9 $x(x + 1)$ **10** $x(x - 2)$
11 $8x(x - 3)$ **12** $7x(5x + 3)$
13 $6x(2 - 3x)$ **14** $ax(x - 4)$
15 $4ax(x + 5)$ **16** $6ax(5x - 3)$
17 $ax(x - a)$ **18** $4ax(3a + 2x)$
19 $5a(3 - 4x^2)$ **20** $3ax(3a - 7x)$

Exercise 4C

1 $5x - 1$ **2** $9x - 3$
3 $8x - 7$ **4** $18x - 13$
5 $6x - 7$ **6** $4x - 9$
7 $4x + 1$ **8** $6 - 5x$
9 $7x - 45$ **10** $6x + 29$
11 20 **12** 9
13 $-8x - 11$ **14** $20 - x$
15 $4x$ **16** $x + 13$
17 $x^2 + 3x - 15$ **18** $x^2 - 3x + 21$
19 $3x^2 + 8x - 6$ **20** $7x^2 - 10x - 10$
21 $6x^2 + 5x - 4$ **22** $10x^2 - 4x - 15$
23 $5x - 5$ **24** 13
25 $5x - 11$ **26** $17x - 5$
27 $9x + 14$ **28** $x - 20$
29 $2x + 2$ **30** 0

Exercise 4D

1 x^9 **2** x^3 **3** x^{10}
4 $14x^8$ **5** $40x^6$ **6** $30x^{13}$
7 $6x^3$ **8** $5x$ **9** $4x^5$
10 $81x^8$ **11** $64x^3$ **12** $21x^6y^7$
13 $20x^9y^5$ **14** $56x^8y^6$ **15** $30x^9y^8$
16 $7x^3y^3$ **17** $3x^4y^7$ **18** $\frac{3}{5}x^5$
19 $4x^3$ **20** $80x^{10}$ **21** $16x^8y^{10}$
22 $40x^{13}y^6$ **23** $3x^2$ **24** $2x^4$
25 $8x^6y^2$

Exercise 4E

1 (a) 9   (b) $1\frac{1}{2}$ (c) $\frac{1}{2}$ (d) 1   (e) 4
2 (a) $\frac{1}{x^3} = x^{-3}$ (b) $x^{-8} = \frac{1}{x^8}$
3 (a) x^{-3} (b) x^{-5} (c) $20x^2$
  (d) x^{-3} (e) x^{-5} (f) x^6
  (g) $4x^{-3}$ (h) $8x^{-3}$ (i) x^{-8}
  (j) x^{15} (k) $\frac{1}{9}x^{-8}$ (l) x^3y^{-3}

Exercise 4F

1 $7n$ **2** $5a$ **3** $56f + 64g$
4 $25 - n$ **5** $36y^{-1}$ **6** $P = 6h$
7 $v = \dfrac{d}{t}$ **8** $A = \frac{1}{2}bh$
9 $C = 500 - 47n$
10 (a) $x = 5$
  (b) Simplifying $7x + 2 - 3x - 5$ gives
    $4x - 3$ so this is an identity.

(c) Expanding $7(x-3)$ gives $7x-21$ so $7(x-3)=7x-21$ is an identity.
(d) $x=-3$
(e) Expanding $6(x-5)$ gives $6x-30$, as does $3(2x-10)$ so identity.
(f) $x=10$
(g) $x=3$
(h) Simplifying $5(x-1)-3(x-2)$ gives $2x+1$ so identity.
(i) Simplifying $7x-2x$ gives $5x$ so identity.
(j) $x=0$

Exercise 4G

1 (a) $8x+40$ **(b)** $21x-28$
(c) $5-30x$ **(d)** $9x^2-2x$
(e) $-8x-20$ **(f)** $6x^2-18x$
(g) $-10x^2+14x$ **(h)** $8ax+3a^2$
(i) $9x-4x^2$
2 (a) $9(x-3)$ **(b)** $7(4x+3)$
(c) $10(x^2-2)$ **(d)** $x(x-1)$
(e) $8x(4x+5)$ **(f)** $8x(3+2x)$
(g) $x(ax-b)$ **(h)** $3ax(2x-3)$
(i) $5ax(5-3x)$
3 (a) $9x-22$ **(b)** $27x-2$
(c) $5x-11$ **(d)** $8x+5$
(e) $19-15x$ **(f)** $10-4x$
(g) x^2+5x+8 **(h)** $9-2x$
4 (a) x^8 **(b)** x^5
(c) x^{15} **(d)** $6x^{10}$
(e) $8x^5$ **(f)** $32x^{15}$
(g) $20x^9y^5$ **(h)** $8x$
(i) $3x^4$
5 (a) 1 **(b)** 3
(c) 1
6 (a) x^{-1} **(b)** $15x^{-9}$
(c) x^{-4} **(d)** $3x^5$
(e) $3x^{-5}$ **(f)** x^{-6}
(g) x^{12} **(h)** $\frac{1}{8}x^{-15}$
7 $180-2a$
8 $A=6d^2$
9 (a) Identity   **(b)** Identity
(c) $x=4$ **(d)** $x=-1$
(e) Identity   **(f)** Identity
10 (a) This equation has no solution.
(b) This equation has no solution.

Exercise 5A

1 (a)

Number of coins	1	2	3	4	5	6
Number of possible outcomes	2	4	8	16	32	64

(b) 1024, the numbers of possible outcomes are powers of 2, the 10th power of 2 is 1024.
(c) 2^n
2 (a) 15, the number of grey tiles in pattern 5 is the 5th triangular number.
(b) 25, the total number of tiles in pattern 5 is the 5th square number.
(c) n^2
(d) (i) $\frac{1}{2}n(n+1)$ **(ii)** $\frac{1}{2}n(n-1)$
(e) Pattern number 12

Exercise 5B

1 (a) (i) 6, 12, 18, 24, 30
(ii) 5, 8, 11, 14, 17
(iii) 4, 11, 18, 25, 32
(iv) 27, 22, 17, 12, 7
(v) 16, 8, 0, -8, -16

(b) (i) 72   **(ii)** 38
(iii) 81   **(iv)** -28
(v) -72
2 (a) $7n$ **(b)** $6n+5$
(c) $n+6$ **(d)** $27-4n$
(e) $8n-3$ **(f)** $13-n$
(g) $41-10n$ **(h)** $7n-21$
3 (a) $2n$ **(b)** $2n-1$
(c) $8n$ **(d)** $2n+8$
(e) $2n+13$ **(f)** $5n+30$

Exercise 5C

1 (a) (i) Shape number 5 has 11 matchsticks, shape number 6 has 13 matchsticks
(ii) Shape number 5 has 16 matchsticks, shape number 6 has 19 matchsticks
(iii) Shape number 5 has 26 matchsticks, shape number 6 has 31 matchsticks
(iv) Shape number 5 has 36 matchsticks, shape number 6 has 43 matchsticks
(b) (i) $2n+1$ **(ii)** $3n+1$
(iii) $5n+1$ **(iv)** $7n+1$
(c) (i) 61 matchsticks
(ii) 91 matchsticks
(iii) 151 matchsticks
(iv) 211 matchsticks
(d) (i) Shape number 105
(ii) Shape number 70
(iii) Shape number 42
(iv) Shape number 30
2 (a) The coefficient is one less than the number of matchsticks in shape number 1. This is because to produce the next shape in the sequence the number of matchsticks we add is one less than the number in shape number 1.
(b) $19n+1$
3 (a) Pattern number 5 has 16 tiles, pattern number 6 has 18 tiles.
(b) $2n+6$
(c) 40 tiles
(d) Pattern number 32
4 (a) Pattern number 5 has 17 dots, pattern number 6 has 20 dots
(b) $3n+2$
(c) 89 dots
(d) Pattern number 36
5 (a) Pattern number 5 has 17 tiles, pattern number 6 has 21 tiles
(b) $4n-3$
(c) 97 tiles
(d) Pattern number 23
(e) Pattern number 15
6 (a) Pattern number 5 has 16 tiles, pattern number 6 has 19 tiles
(b) $3n+1$
(c) 85 tiles
(d) Pattern number 43
(e) Pattern number 26

Exercise 5D

1 $d=vt$
2 $T=30W+30$
3 (a) $e=\dfrac{360}{n}$ **(b)** $i=180-\dfrac{360}{n}$
4 $E=\frac{1}{2}kx^2$

5 $V=\frac{1}{2}Sr$
6 (a) $A=\frac{1}{24}P^2$ **(b)** $V=\frac{1}{1728}P^3$

Exercise 5E

1 $y=-5$ **2** $V=240$
3 $A=209$ (3 s.f.)   **4** $s=6.6$
5 $F=-40$ **6** $A=37.5$
7 $A=670$ (3 s.f.)   **8** $v=-13$
9 $d=5.35$ (3 s.f.)   **10** $A=59.4$ (3 s.f.)
11 $y=7$ **12** $s=67\frac{1}{2}$
13 $d=125.05$ **14** $D=54$
15 $H=10.5$ **16** $E=-127.5$
17 $A=147$ (3 s.f.)   **18** $y=-4$
19 $v=-3.9$ **20** $F=304.2$
21 $V=12\,200$ (3 s.f.)
22 $d=270$ **23** $P=28.5$
24 $R=0.0021$ **25** $A=2257.8125$
26 $v=21.6$ (3 s.f.)   **27** $D=16$ (2 s.f.)
28 $T=14.3$ (3 s.f.)   **29** $v=13.8$ (3 s.f.)
30 $v=160$

Exercise 5F

1 $x=-2$ **2** $R=48$
3 $r=3.45$ (3 s.f.)   **4** $a=9.3$
5 $C=35$ **6** $b=19$
7 $r=3.45$ (3 s.f.)   **8** $t=3.6$
9 $C=18.5$ (3 s.f.)   **10** $d=10.4$ (3 s.f.)
11 $x=\pm4$ **12** $u=9$
13 $A=9$ **14** $u=7$
15 $x=-3$ **16** $v=5$
17 $r=3.63$ (3 s.f.)   **18** $h=3.2$
19 $h=5.78$ **20** $x=15$

Exercise 5G

1 (a) (i) 2, 11, 20, 29, 38
(ii) 11, 19, 27, 35, 43
(iii) 34, 28, 22, 16, 10
(iv) -1, -4, -7, -10, -13
(b) (i) 173   **(ii)** 163
(iii) -80 **(iv)** -58
2 (a) $7n-4$ **(b)** $23-3n$
(c) $8n+5$ **(d)** $10-5n$
3 (a) Shape number 5 has 26 matchsticks, shape number 6 has 31 matchsticks
(b) $5n+1$
(c) 116 matchsticks
(d) Shape number 11
(e) Shape number 39
4 (a) Pattern number 5 has 21 tiles, pattern number 6 has 25 tiles
(b) $3n+1$
(c) $4n+1$
(d) 37 octagonal tiles
(e) 101 tiles in total
(f) 40 octagonal tiles
(g) 77 tiles in total
5 (a) $T=8x+4h$
(b) Rearranging gives $h=\dfrac{T-8x}{4}$
(c) $V=\dfrac{x^2(T-8x)}{4}$
6 (a) $e=53$ **(b)** $R=9$
7 (a) $y=17$ **(b)** $x=7$
8 (a) $L=64.2$ (3 s.f.) **(b)** $r=3.4$ (2 s.f.)
9 (a) $I=7.5$ **(b)** $d=20$
10 (a) $r=2.36$ (3 s.f.) **(b)** $A=290$ (3 s.f.)
11 (a) $V=1430$ (3 s.f.)
(b) $R=7.3$ (2 s.f.)
12 $A=54$

Exercise 6A

1
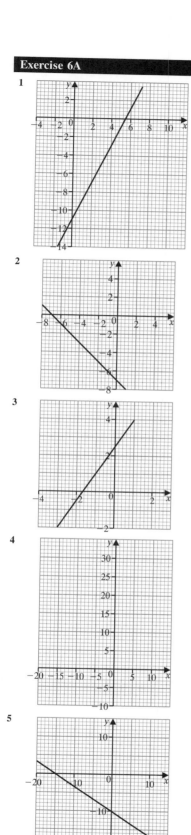

2

3

4

5

6
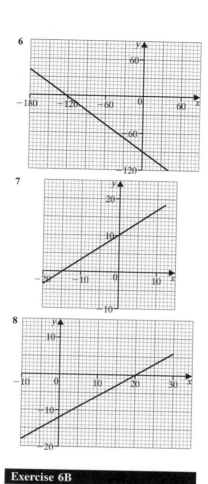

7

8

Exercise 6B

1
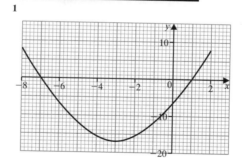

2
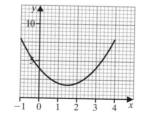

3
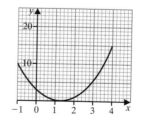

4

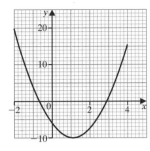

5

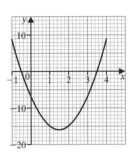

6

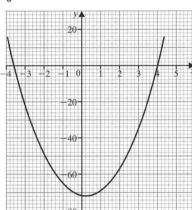

7

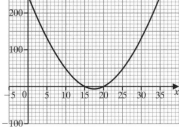

8

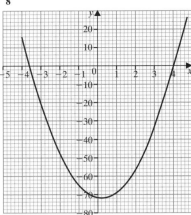

9

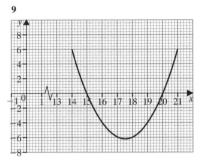

10

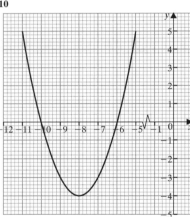

11

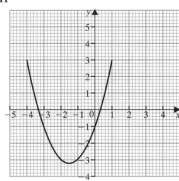

Exercise 6C

1 From 6 am to about 8 am there is a large increase in the traffic flow (possibly due to people driving to work). It then decreases until about 10 am (most people will need to be at work for 9 am, so as more people arrive at work, there will be less traffic on the roads). During the rest of the morning and early afternoon the traffic flow is at a constant rate. Then at about 4 pm the flow increases to a peak at 6 pm, similar to the morning (this could be because of people driving home after work).

2 At first, as weight is added the spring extends at a constant rate. In fact the extension is linearly proportioned to the weight added. Then after a certain amount of weight has been added, adding more weight extends the spring by more for the same amount of weight added, and this continues so that as we add on more weight the spring extends at an increasing rate.

3 Prices steadily increase from 1980 to a peak about 1987 when suddenly the prices decrease at about the same rate as the increase. The decrease continues and slows to about 1995, when the prices begin to increase again. The increase becomes faster up to the year 2000.

4 The car is travelling at a constant speed at the start of this part of the journey. It continues at this speed for a while and then slows down until it stops. The car is then at rest for a short period of time.

5

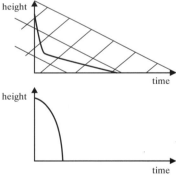

Exercise 7A

1 (a) $a = 19.2$ cm (3 s.f.)
  (b) $b = 11.7$ cm (3 s.f.)
  (c) $c = 7.40$ cm (3 s.f.)
  (d) $d = 16.8$ cm (3 s.f.)
  (e) $e = 3.14$ cm (3 s.f.)
  (f) $f = 8.49$ cm (3 s.f.)

2 (a) $AB = 5$
  (b) $AB = 15$
  (c) $AB = 8.06$ (3 s.f.)
  (d) $AB = 5$
  (e) $AB = 3.61$ (3 s.f.)
  (f) $AB = 8.94$ (3 s.f.)

3 (a) $a = 8$ cm
  (b) $b = 12.0$ cm (3 s.f.)
  (c) $c = 6.29$ cm (3 s.f.)
  (d) $d = 4.86$ cm (3 s.f.)

4 30.5 cm (3 s.f.)
5 10.9 cm (3 s.f.)
6 (a) $x = 12.8$ cm (3 s.f.),
        $y = 18.0$ cm (3 s.f.)
    (b) $x = 24$ cm
    (c) $x = 13.7$ cm (3 s.f.),
        $y = 24.3$ cm (3 s.f.)
    (d) $x = 12$ cm, $y = 23.3$ cm (3 s.f.)

Exercise 7B

1

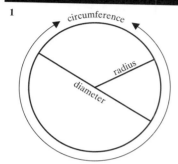

2

circumference
arc
tangent

3

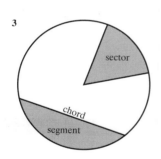

sector
chord
segment

Exercise 7C

1 $PO = 13$ cm
2 $SO = 17.3$ cm (3 s.f.)
3 $\angle POR = 74°$
4 $\angle POQ = 64°$

Exercise 7D

1 (a) $a = 12.0$ cm (3 s.f.)
    (b) $b = 24$ cm
2 (a) 7.21 (3 s.f.)   (b) 7.07 (3 s.f.)
3 $AB = 6.15$ cm (3 s.f.)
4 28.6 cm (3 s.f.)
5 $SP = 13.9$ cm (3 s.f.), $\angle POR = 60°$
6 7.28 m (3 s.f.)
7 17.2 km (3 s.f.)
8 10.6 cm (3 s.f.)

Exercise 8A

1 (a) 0.799 (3 s.f.)   (b) 1
    (c) 0.5   (d) 1
    (e) 0.208 (3 s.f.)   (f) 0.208 (3 s.f.)
    (g) 0.601 (3 s.f.)   (h) 0.743 (3 s.f.)
    (i) 0.731 (3 s.f.)   (j) 0.946 (3 s.f.)
    (k) 2.61 (3 s.f.)   (l) 0.934 (3 s.f.)
2 (a) 45.0° (3 s.f.)   (b) 72.0° (3 s.f.)
    (c) 56.0° (3 s.f.)   (d) 24.0° (3 s.f.)
    (e) 7.07° (3 s.f.)   (f) 12.0° (3 s.f.)
3 (a) $a = 53.1°$ (3 s.f.)
    (b) $b = 17.4°$ (3 s.f.)
    (c) $c = 46.7°$ (3 s.f.)
    (d) $d = 18.4°$ (3 s.f.)
    (e) $e = 46.6°$ (3 s.f.)
    (f) $f = 30°$
    (g) $g = 74.5°$ (3 s.f.)
    (h) $h = 54.3°$ (3 s.f.)

Exercise 8B

(a) $a = 6.55$ cm (3 s.f.)
(b) $b = 7.53$ cm (3 s.f.)
(c) $c = 7.64$ (3 s.f.)
(d) $d = 6.79$ cm (3 s.f.)
(e) $e = 24.8$ cm (3 s.f.)
(f) $f = 14.1$ cm (3 s.f.)
(g) $g = 2.45$ cm (3 s.f.)
(h) $h = 61.0$ cm (3 s.f.)
(i) $i = 13.3$ cm (3 s.f.)
(j) $j = 2.91$ cm (3 s.f.)

Exercise 8C

1 (a) $a = 28.3$ cm (3 s.f.)
    (b) $b = 8.64$ cm (3 s.f.)
2 14.0 km (3 s.f.)
3 (a) 2.62 m (3 s.f.)
    (b) 6.49 m (3 s.f.)
4 23.2 m (3 s.f.)
5 (a) 30.8 km (3 s.f.)
    (b) 216° (3 s.f.)
6 (a) $DC = 3.69$ m (3 s.f.)
    (b) $\angle DAB = 34.6°$ (3 s.f.)
7 46.7 km

Exercise 9A

1 Translation **A** to **B** is $\begin{pmatrix} -6 \\ -4 \end{pmatrix}$

Translation **A** to **C** is $\begin{pmatrix} -1 \\ -4 \end{pmatrix}$

Translation **A** to **D** is $\begin{pmatrix} -3 \\ -8 \end{pmatrix}$

Translation **A** to **E** is $\begin{pmatrix} 2 \\ -10 \end{pmatrix}$

Translation **A** to **F** is $\begin{pmatrix} 3 \\ 1 \end{pmatrix}$

Translation **A** to **G** is $\begin{pmatrix} -5 \\ -10 \end{pmatrix}$

2

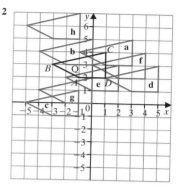

Exercise 9B

1 (a)

(b)

(c)

(d)

2 (a) Reflection in line $y = -x$
    (b) Reflection in $y = 0$
    (c) Reflection in $x = -1$
    (d) Reflection in $x = 1$

Exercise 9C

1

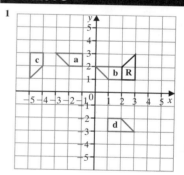

2 (a) Rotation centre $(\frac{1}{2}, -\frac{1}{2})$ through $-90°$
    (b) Rotation centre $(0, 0)$ through $+180°$
    (c) Rotation centre $(0, 3)$ through $-90°$
    (d) Rotation centre $(3, 0)$ through $-90°$

3

Rotation	Transforms
centre $(0, 0)$, 90°	point $(1, 2)$ to $(-2, 1)$
centre $(0, 0)$, $-180°$	point $(3, 5)$ to $(-3, -5)$
centre $(-1, 2)$, $-90°$	point $(2, 3)$ to $(0, -1)$
centre $(2, 4)$, 270°	point $(2, -1)$ to $(-3, 4)$
centre $(0, 0)$, $-270°$	point $(-1, 4)$ to $(-4, -1)$

Exercise 9D

1
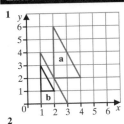

2
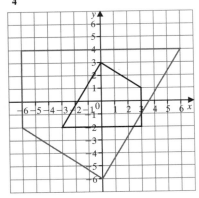

3 (a) Enlargement scale factor $3\frac{1}{2}$, centre $(\frac{3}{5}, \frac{1}{5})$
(b) Enlargement scale factor -1, centre $(0,0)$
(c) Enlargement scale factor 2, centre $(2,0)$
(d) Enlargement scale factor 3, centre $(\frac{1}{2}, 4\frac{1}{2})$
(e) Enlargement scale factor $-1\frac{1}{2}$, centre $(-1, 2\frac{2}{5})$

4

Exercise 10A

1 $BC = 37$ cm
2 (a) 96 cm² (b) 34.72 cm²
(c) 16 cm²
3 (a) $x = 6$ cm (b) $x = 5$ cm
(c) $x = 5$ cm

---

4 (a) 30 cm² (b) 7.9 cm²
(c) 13.2 cm² (d) 12 cm²
(e) 84 cm²
5 (a) 36 cm² (b) 32.5 m²
(c) 34 cm²
6 $\dfrac{12x^2}{5}$
7 (a) 1764π cm²
(b) 53.3 (3 s.f.)

Exercise 10B

1 (a) 34 cm²
(b) 70 cm²
(c) 49.5 cm²
(d) 135.45 cm² (2 d.p.)
(e) 81.46 cm² (2 d.p.)
(e) 85.84 cm² (2 d.p.)

Exercise 10C

1 4 cm
2 112 cm²
3

Size	Volume	Area
1, 1, 13	13	54
1, 2, 12	24	76
2, 2, 11	44	96
1, 3, 11	33	94
2, 3, 10	60	112
1, 4, 10	40	108
3, 3, 9	81	126
2, 4, 9	72	124

Size	Volume	Area
1, 5, 9	45	118
3, 4, 8	96	136
2, 5, 8	80	132
1, 6, 8	48	124
4, 4, 7	112	144
3, 5, 7	105	142
2, 6, 7	84	136
1, 7, 7	49	126
4, 5, 6	120	148
3, 6, 6	108	144
5, 5, 5	125	150

Maximum volume when edges are 5 cm, 5 cm, 5 cm
Maximum surface area when edges are 5 cm, 5 cm, 5 cm

4

Height	Length	Width	Volume
5	3	2	30
7	8	5	280
4	8	3	96
5	7	3	105
10	3.5	3	105

Exercise 10D

1 Surface area = 150 cm², volume = 90 cm³
2 $BE = 5$ cm, surface area = 320 cm²
3 (a) Volume = 500 cm³, surface area = 400 cm²

(b) Volume = 6.75 m³, surface area = 24.4 m² (1 d.p.)
4 2806.86 m³ (2 d.p.)
5 Surface area = 565.9 m² (4 s.f.), volume = 1319 m³ (4 s.f.)

Exercise 10E

1 (a) radius 1.55 cm (3 s.f.)
(b) radius 2.06 cm (3 s.f.)
(c) radius 2.60 cm (3 s.f.)
(d) radius 1.46 cm (3 s.f.)
(e) radius 1.91 cm (3 s.f.)
2 (a) 300π cm³ (b) 512π cm³
(c) 180π cm³ (d) 3200π cm³
(e) 63.48π cm³
3 (a) Surface area = 478 cm², volume = 754 cm³
(b) Surface area = 1280 cm², volume = 3170 cm³
(c) Surface area = 6440 cm², volume = 15 700 cm³
(d) Surface area = 99.0 cm², volume = 63.6 cm³
(e) Surface area = 4750 cm², volume = 5890 cm³
(f) Surface area = 567 000 cm², volume = 226 000 cm³

Exercise 10F

1 60 000 cm³
2 4.99 g (3 s.f.)
3 $16.666\frac{2}{3}$ revolutions
4 56 500 g (3 s.f.)
5 9.42 l (3 s.f.)
6 134 sheets are needed, so 13.4 booklets

Exercise 10G

1 162 l
2 11.2 gallons
3 1089 pence per kilogram
4 1.78 km per litre (3 s.f.)
5 0.045 pounds per cubic foot (3 d.p.)
6 4 m²

Exercise 10H

1 8000 kg **2** 4500 g
3 5000 bricks **4** 25 m s⁻¹
5 12 tonnes

Exercise 10I

1 (a) 84 cm² (b) 126 cm²
2 (a) 8910 cm² (3 s.f.)
(b) 16 300 cm² (3 s.f.)
3 22.0 m² (3 s.f.)
4 Volume = 8580 cm³ (3 s.f.) surface area = 5480 cm² (3 s.f.)
5 Volume = 2680 cm³ (3 s.f.) surface area = 1250 cm² (3 s.f.)
6

Thickness	Length	Width	Volume
12 mm	1.8 m	5 cm	1080 cm³
9 mm	2.4 m	8 cm	1728 cm³
15 mm	3.0 m	20 cm	9000 cm³
5 cm	8.0 m	5 cm	0.02 m³

Exercise 11A

1 (a), (b)

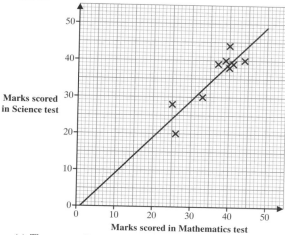

Marks scored in Science test / **Marks scored in Mathematics test**

(c) The scatter diagram shows positive correlation.
(d) The estimate is 35 marks in the Science test.
2 (a) The scatter diagram shows negative correlation.
(b)

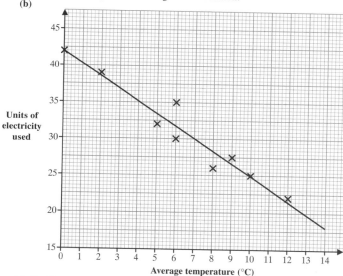

Units of electricity used / **Average temperature (°C)**

(c) (i) The estimate is 5.3°C.
(ii) The estimate is 35 units of electricity.
3 (a) The scatter diagram shows negative correlation.
(b)

Life expectancy (years) / **Birth rate**

(c) The estimate is a life expectancy of 53 years.

Exercise 11B

1 (a) 237.5 g
(b) $200 < w \leqslant 300$
(c) $100 < w \leqslant 200$
(d) No, we have no information on the spread of weights of potatoes in the second bag.
2 (a) Estimate mean speed is 38.4 mph (3 s.f.)
(b) $40 < s \leqslant 50$
(c) $30 < s \leqslant 40$
(d) 37 cars
(e) As we do not know the spread of the speeds of the vehicles in the second survey, we cannot say whether the conclusion is correct or not.
3 (a) 26 to 30
(b) 11 to 15
(c) Estimate for mean number of marks is 16.3

Exercise 11C

1 (a)

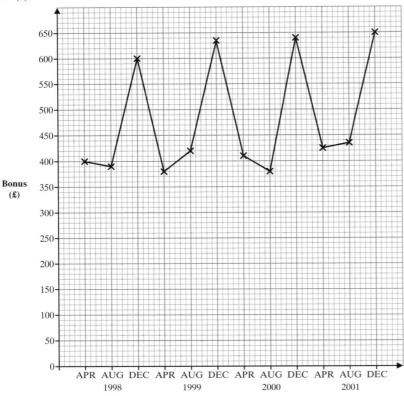

(b) Moving averages:

1st	2nd	3rd	4th	5th	6th	7th	8th	9th	10th
$463\frac{1}{3}$	$456\frac{2}{3}$	$466\frac{2}{3}$	$478\frac{1}{3}$	$488\frac{1}{3}$	475	$476\frac{2}{3}$	$481\frac{2}{3}$	500	$503\frac{1}{3}$

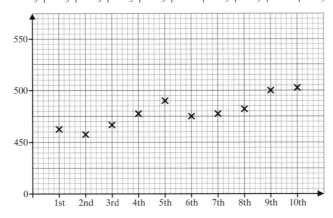

(c) The graphs show there is a slight increase in Jon's bonus over
the period from April 1998 to December 2001.

2 (a)

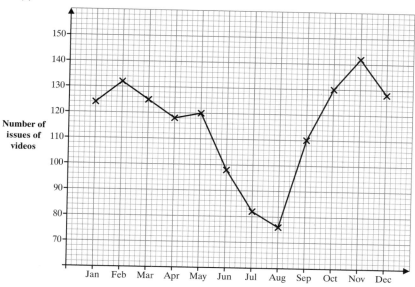

(b) Moving averages:

1st	2nd	3rd	4th	5th	6th	7th	8th	9th
124.75	123.75	115.25	104.5	94	91.5	99.5	114.5	127.5

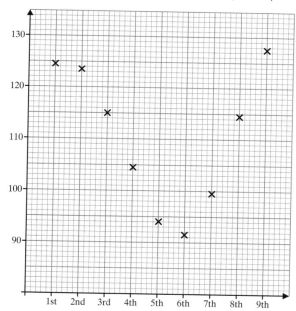

(c) The number of issues of videos falls during the first half of the year and then rises at the end of the year.

3 (a)

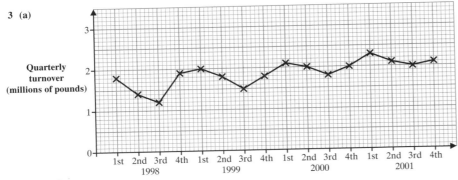

(b) Moving averages:

1st	2nd	3rd	4th	5th	6th	7th	8th	9th	10th	11th	12th	13th
1.575	1.625	1.725	1.8	1.775	1.8	1.85	1.925	1.975	2.025	2.05	2.1	2.125

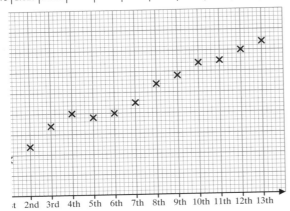

(c) The company's turnover has increased over the years 1998 to 2001 inclusive.

4 (a)

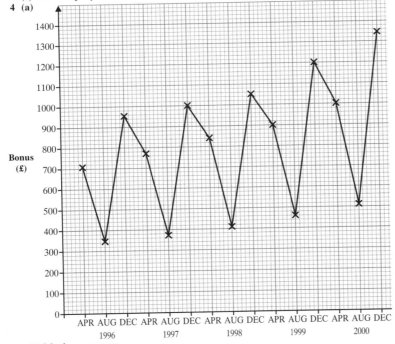

(b) Moving averages:

1st	2nd	3rd	4th	5th	6th	7th	8th	9th	10th	11th	12th	13th
$666\frac{2}{3}$	$690\frac{1}{2}$	$699\frac{1}{3}$	715	738	$751\frac{1}{3}$	$783\frac{2}{3}$	804	$820\frac{1}{3}$	$854\frac{1}{3}$	$888\frac{2}{3}$	906	$954\frac{1}{3}$

(c)

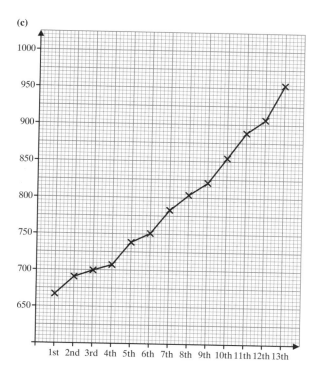

(d) Sandra's bonus has increased over the years 1996 to 2000 inclusive.

Exercise 12A

1 (a)

Number of darts thrown	Cumulative frequency
Up to 5	10
Up to 10	27
Up to 15	38
Up to 20	43
Up to 25	55
Up to 30	75

(b) See illustration opposite
(c) (i) Median = 15 darts
   (ii) Upper quartile = 25 darts,
      lower quartile = 8 darts
   (iii) Interquartile range = 17 darts
   (iv) 25%

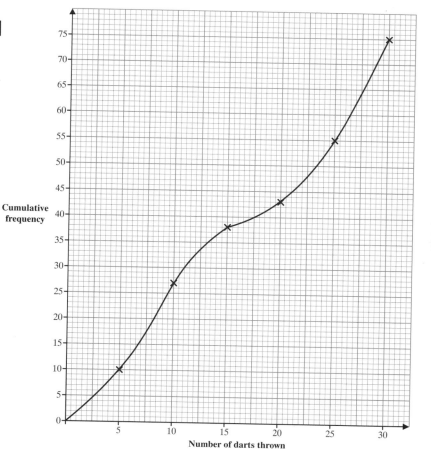

(d)

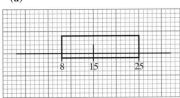

(e) The median number of darts thrown at Streetfield School is greater than the median number of darts thrown at Harwell School. However, the interquartile range at Streetfield School is greater than at Harwell School, so there could be a significant number of competitors at Streetfield School throwing fewer darts than the lower quartile number of darts thrown at Harwell School — or, similarly, a significant number of competitors throwing more darts than the upper quartile number of darts thrown at Harwell School. We cannot make any definite statement on which competition has the best quality of dart throwing.

2 (a)

Waiting time in seconds	Cumulative frequency
Up to 60	4
Up to 120	12
Up to 180	22
Up to 240	40
Up to 300	70
Up to 360	80

(b) See illustration opposite
(c) (i) Median = 240 seconds
    (ii) Interquartile range = 108 seconds

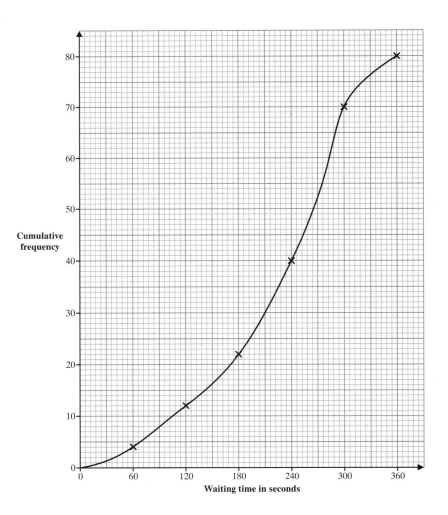

(d)

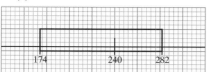

174   240   282

3 (a)

Weekly rainfall in mm	Cumulative frequency
Up to 10	18
Up to 20	38
Up to 30	44
Up to 40	47
Up to 50	50
Up to 60	52

(b)

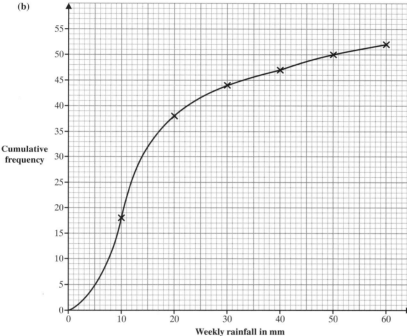

(c) Median = 13 mm
(d) Interquartile range = 15 mm
(e) 22 weeks

(f)

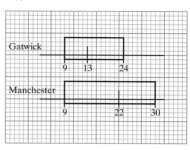

The box plots for Gatwick and Manchester airports show that the median weekly rainfall at Manchester is greater than the median weekly rainfall at Gatwick. In fact, the median weekly rainfall at Manchester is only just less than the upper quartile weekly rainfall at Gatwick, so there is a very significant number of weeks at Manchester with weekly rainfall greater than the upper quartile weekly rainfall at Gatwick. We can say with confidence that the weekly rainfall in Manchester is generally greater than at Gatwick. Any comment about the lower quartiles is inconclusive.

4 (a) The interquartile range for boys is larger than that for girls. The median weight for boys is higher than the median weight for girls; in fact, the median weight for boys is higher than the upper quartile weight for girls, so there is a very significant number of boys with weights greater than the upper quartile weight for girls. The lower quartile weight for boys is higher than the median weight for girls, so there can be relatively few boys with a weight less than the median weight for girls. We can say with confidence that the boys in the sample are generally heavier than the girls.

(b)

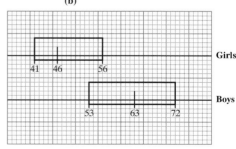

(c) (i) **7.5%**
    (ii) 48.75%

Exercise 12B

1 (a)

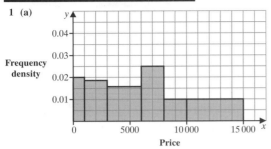

(b)

Price (p) in £	Frequency
$0 < p \leqslant 1000$	20
$1000 < p \leqslant 3000$	36
$3000 < p \leqslant 6000$	48
$6000 < p \leqslant 8000$	50
$8000 < p \leqslant 10\,000$	20
$10\,000 < p \leqslant 15\,000$	50

2 (a)

Homework time (t) minutes	Frequency
$20 < t \leqslant 25$	20
$25 < t \leqslant 40$	14
$40 < t \leqslant 60$	12
$60 < t \leqslant 85$	6
$85 < t \leqslant 90$	16

2 (b) There are 58 students.

3

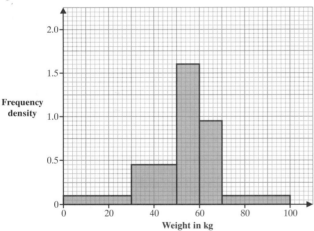

Exercise 12C

1 Examples: use calculator to pick random page, column on a page, line in a column then word in line. Make decisions beforehand about: whether or not to include words in quotations; whether or not to include article titles, picture captions, etc.; what to do about pages where text is arranged randomly (do you ignore the page ?).

2 Clearly this outlier *is* against the trend so including it as it stands would distort any results and conclusions (e.g. line of best fit). One possibility would be to ignore the datum point completely, continuing with the other points.

However, depending on the specifics there could be an explanation for the outlier, for example a young car with a high mileage would have a low value, in which case we must decide whether to include the point or not. We would have to decide whether the point was typical of the survey (why disregard it just because it doesn't fit?), or atypical so that we feel justified in excluding it.

3 Mean is 6.5

Examination style practice paper

Section 1

1

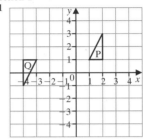

2 (a) $4n + 2$
  (b) Pattern number 12

3 $1\frac{13}{15}$

4 (a) c^{-4} (b) $12p^5q^6$

5

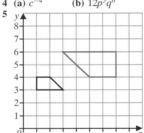

6

Time (t) in minutes	Frequency
$0 \leqslant t < 10$	8
$10 \leqslant t < 15$	12
$15 \leqslant t < 20$	7
$20 \leqslant t < 30$	6

7 $n = 5$

Section 2

1 68%

2 Moving averages:

	1st	2nd
	£1679	£2407

3 (a) $3x^3 + 4x$ (b) 13

4 $36.5°$ (1 d.p.)

5 $x = -3$

6 $BD = 6.25\,\text{cm}$ (3 s.f.)